Basic Construction Refresher

D1373709

HONDROS LEARNING™
4140 Executive Parkway
Westerville, Ohio 43081
www.hondroslearning.com

19 18 17 16   1 2 3 4

ISBN: 978-1-59844-282-3

For more information on or to purchase our products, please visit www.hondroslearning.com.

TABLE OF CONTENTS

Table of Contents

# PREFACE

Basic Construction Refresher

The *Basic Construction Refresher* course is designed for real estate agents and appraisers to review fundamental construction methods, both old and new, in residential real estate. The course covers construction from site preparation through completion. Major components of a house are identified including building materials and mechanical systems. Further, the course reveals 'red flags' that are discernible to agents and appraisers when inspecting a home for a listing, sale, or valuation. Finally, the course describes how physical and functional issues in houses affect value.

Course Learning Objectives

- Describe the building envelope and how it can be breached.
- Identify types of foundation systems.
- Describe the attributes of different types of soil.
- Identify types of construction techniques.
- Classify houses by the type of construction.
- Recognize exterior materials used on houses.
- Identify common roof styles and roofing terms.
- Recognize basic roofing components.
- Recall materials used for roofing, gutters, and downspouts.
- Describe interior building materials used in houses.
- Identify materials used for exterior and interior doors.
- Describe common types of windows installed in houses.
- Describe the functions of a residential plumbing system.
- Identify types of plumbing pipe materials.
- Recall common contaminates in water and purifying methods.
- Describe how a residential septic system operates.
- Identify types of residential HVAC systems.
- Explain the importance of proper ventilation in houses.
- Identify inventions and contributions that lead to modern electrical household systems and appliances.
- Explain the basic way household electricity functions.
- Explain the potential dangers of electrical wiring and the importance of grounding.
- Explain why 'green' features are important in housing.
- Identify the methods and materials used to ensure houses are energy efficient.
- Identify the causes and potential hazards of poor indoor air quality.
- Explain testing methods and remedies for indoor environmental hazards.
- Recognize house designs and attributes of various house styles.
- Differentiate functional depreciation, physical depreciation, and external obsolescence.

Hondros Learning

Hondros Learning™ is a leading provider of classroom materials for appraisal pre-licensing and continuing education. Together with Hondros College, we have provided training and educational products for more than one million students. For more information about CompuCram online exam-prep products or any of our other products, please visit www.hondroslearning.com and, www.compucram.com.

Acknowledgments

Hondros Learning™ thanks the following expert for her valuable contributions and assistance in developing this text:

Melanie J. McLane
Certified Appraiser

Melanie McLane is a practicing appraiser, broker, and educator. With over 34 years in the business, she has vast experience in all aspects of real estate. She devotes most of her time to teaching, writing, and consulting with real estate companies, but keeps her licenses active and continues to list, sell, and appraise in order to keep her thumb on the market. A graduate of Kenyon College, she has the following designations: ABR, CDEI, CRB, CRS, ePRO, Green-Certified, GRI, RAA, RSPS, SRS and SRES.

Chapter 1:
The Building Envelope and Foundations

Introduction

In this chapter, we will explore the building envelope and common breaches that affect it. We will also discuss foundations as well as the soils that foundations rest on, which are critically important for proper support of the house. Finally, we will cover common practices in new construction to avoid foundation issues.

Objectives

After completing this chapter, students will be able to:

- Describe the building envelope.
- Identify types of foundation systems.
- Classify major types of soils.
- List common issues with soils and foundations.

Building Envelope The entire building, from footer to roof. It encloses the living area and should provide protection from the elements.

Footer The support for the foundation of a building. Footers are installed below the frost line, and are wider than the foundations that they support.

Foundation The support for a building. It can be constructed of stone, poured concrete, pre-engineered concrete walls, concrete block, or even wood.

Infestation Usually from insects, one of the many things that can compromise the building envelope.

Lally Column A post, made of metal, with a screw type device at the top, designed to be placed in a basement to provide additional support for the house.

Soil Types A reference to the types of soil houses are built on; homes must be properly engineered for the soil type.

Key Terms

The Building Envelope

The **building envelope** of a house is *everything from the foundation to the roof.* It is what contains the house, making the division between inside and outside. The function of the building envelope is to protect the inhabitants from the weather, keep them comfortable and safe, and provide elements needed to live in the house.

Figure 1.1: Building Envelope

Water and Air Issues

A building envelope can be breached in many ways:

- Water infiltration into basements and crawl spaces
- Water infiltration through the roof, windows, or doors
- Air infiltration, which can make the house too cold or too hot, from breaches in the basement, slab, walls, windows, doors, crawl spaces, or attic

However, as much as we want the building envelope to protect the inhabitants from the elements, it should not be too airtight. Indoor air quality has been measured at two (2) to five (5) times worse than outdoor air quality. Many times, homeowners, in their attempt to keep their homes either warm or cool, make the building envelope too tight, and do not allow for proper air circulation.

Mold

Another issue with indoor air quality is mold, which is found in every home, but can be toxic if it is the wrong kind of mold, or there is too much of it. This will be discussed in Chapter 9: Environmental Issues.

Home Infestation

A home can be compromised through infestation by insects or animals.

- Common infestation problems are termites, carpenter bees, and carpenter ants. Carpenter bees and ants drill up through exterior areas, such as railings and other spots. Evidence of infestation is small piles of sawdust.

- Animal infestation includes mice, rats, squirrels, bats, and occasionally other small mammals, including skunks.

Termites

Termites often get into a house from wood being placed directly on the soil. Homeowners have inadvertently invited termites into their homes by storing firewood inside the house or up against the outside, or by using wood chip mulch around the foundation. In the Southern United States, ridding a home of termite infestation requires 'tenting' of the house for several days.

There are actually **four kinds of termites** found in the United States:

1. **Drywood termites** are found in regions that do not reach freezing temperatures during the winter. The Deep South, extending from Florida to California, is in this category.

2. **Subterranean termites** are in every state but Alaska and can withstand a wide range of temperatures. Alaska has the distinction of being "termite free."

3. **Formosan termites** are primarily found in southern states, as well as Hawaii; they have been found as far north as Tennessee.

4. **Dampwood termites** are mostly found in Florida, the Southwest, and the Pacific Coast. They do not typically infest building structures.

Foundations

All properties are built on a **foundation**. The foundation can be a slab, a crawl space, or a full or partial basement. A **footer** is *the structural item on which the foundation of the property rests*. Footers must provide a firm foundation that will withstand the forces of nature, which include gravity, frost heaving, hydrostatic pressure, and soil swelling. Footers transmit the load of the structure to the soil. Any well-built building will spread the load as much as possible to horizontal sections that can hold the load.

Commonly, in residential construction, footers are:

- Two to three times the thickness of the wall supported by the footer, or more, depending upon soil type and the weight of the building above.

- Installed below the frost line.

- Separate from the foundation.

- Poured concrete, reinforced with steel called rebar.

  √ **Note:** Poured concrete and rebar in residential construction is a 20th century technique. Reinforced concrete was actually patented in 1867, by Joseph Monier, a French gardener.

In **stem-wall foundations**, *concrete footings are installed below grade, and then concrete block walls, called "stem-walls," are installed on top of the footers to just above grade.* The slab is then poured on compacted fill dirt inside the perimeter of the foundation wall. This is a technique that can offer more protection against water infiltration in hurricane prone areas.

In parts of the United States that are warm climates, such as Florida, and are also hurricane prone, builders may use **monolithic construction**, where *the footer and foundation walls are poured together as one.* In non-hurricane prone areas, a slab for the basement floor is poured over compacted gravel placed within the footer, as seen here.

Figure 1.2: Compacted Gravel

Notice the square area of concrete in the photo. The common term for this is a "deadman," which is a footer in place to hold up a post in the basement. Many homes have issues with foundations because posts were installed *after* the house was constructed, and the posts do not have a footer supporting them. Without a footer supporting them, the weight of the house presses down on the post, which drives the post into the earth.

Things to look for...

Look for cracks or the post sinking as evidence of no footer.

Posts and Lally Columns

Posts, or **Lally columns**, were used in older houses, without footers under the posts. Notice that the Lally columns can be extended through a screw-like apparatus at the top. Homeowners would seek to level out a house by turning the mechanism very slowly, over a long period of time, which was believed to not create issues in the upper floors. Often, it didn't work. The downward pressure from the house is very evident.

In the bottom picture, you can see how the metal plate at the top of the Lally column is bent out of shape. In both these cases, the house is 'out of square' with doorways and windows that are not square, floors that are on a slant, and other easily seen problems.

Figure 1.3: Left, Lally Column with Bent Plate; right, Lally Column Mechanism

Stone Foundations

Throughout the United States, older houses exist, some over 300 years old. These were built with whatever materials were handy. It is common in older homes, especially in the New England and the Middle Atlantic States, to see stone foundations, also called "laid stone" foundations. Some mortar materials were added, but these foundations were often not water tight. The footers for these foundations are also stone.

Wood Foundations

Wood foundations, although not common, are found in some residential construction. Most real estate agents report a strong resistance to these types of foundations. They are not as durable as concrete foundations, and the soils around them must be kept dry.

Pre-cast Foundations

A type of foundation that has gained in popularity over the past few decades is the **pre-engineered**, or **pre-cast foundation**. Manufacturers describe these as a "footer that is the wall."

These foundations:

- Are guaranteed to be waterproof by many manufacturers.
- Are pre-cast in a factory, rebar reinforced, pre-insulated, and pre-studded with holes drilled in the studs for future wiring.
- Are often installed directly on compacted gravel, much like a railroad bed, as opposed to on a traditional footer.
- Can be installed any time of year, and go up quickly, usually in less than a day.
- Are popular with modular home builders, because they are always 'square.'

Block Wall Foundations

Concrete block wall foundations are typically reinforced with rebar positioned in the holes of the blocks, which are filled with concrete. A concrete block wall can end up not being square due to human error.

Poured Foundations

Some builders use poured concrete foundations. A mold, or form, is delivered to the site and the concrete, which is reinforced with rebar, is poured into the molds.

Soils

Different types of soil require different construction techniques and safeguards. Part of the job of building a house is determining what soils are on the property and either amending the soil by mixing other soils into it, or compacting it, or digging down to a level of another kind of soil.

Soils are classified a number of ways, including:

- Loam
- Cohesive (Clay)
- Rock

- Organic
- Sand
- Fill

 Note: "Fill" is soil, or other materials, brought onto a site to fill in holes, or to bring it up to a specific level. If the fill is not compacted property, it will create foundation issues.

Soil Pros and Cons

Builder classifications for soil include:

PROS AND CONS OF SOILS		
Soil Type	**Pros**	**Cons**
Organic (river bottom)	• Great for growing flowers and vegetables • Contracts on its own	• Does not compress easily • Very difficult to build on
Granular (gravel, sand, or silt)	• Best for building on • Drains easily • Compacts easily • Bet load bearing properties	• No cohesive strength
Cohesive (clay)	• Has cohesive strength • Can be excavated with vertical side slopes	• Contracts and expands and may harden over time • Has lower load bearing qualities than granular soil • Poor for gardens

Table 1.1: Pros and Cons of Soil

Water Issues

Water and soils don't necessarily mix well. Here are some common issues:

- **Hydrostatic pressure** – Can literally collapse a basement wall from the pressure. Homes built on hillsides or the sides of mountains usually experience some form of hydrostatic pressure; for example, when the snow cover begins to melt in the spring. This can lead to rockslides.

- **Limestone deposits** – Over time, water erodes limestone, causing sinkholes. This illustration shows how a sinkhole is formed. Certain parts of the United States, most notably Florida, have many sinkholes.

Sinkhole Development

As rains falls, it absorbs carbon dioxide, making percolating water slightly acidic. As this water migrates downward, the carbonate bedrock is slowly dissolved creating bedrock voids

Over time, the underground void becomes larger as soil and rock from above fall into the cavity and are washed away.

The void continues to grow and slope upward toward the surface.

Eventually, the structural integrity of the overlying material is breached and a sink hole forms.

Figure 1.4: Sinkhole Development; Illustration Courtesy of Missouri Department of Natural Resources

- **How much water the soil will absorb and hold** – Some types of soils, such as peat, retain a very large percentage of water, making them unsuitable for building. Sandy soils generally drain well, but building on sand can be tricky, and can require the use of pilings to get the support needed.

Signs of Foundation Issues

What are the visual signs of foundation issues? Here's what you might observe:

1. Walls separating from the floor or foundation; may be visible inside or outside
2. Cracks in brick, either in exterior or interior
3. Moldings that are cracked or separated; wallpaper that has shifted (a border no longer meets the ceiling)
4. Floors that are uneven or slope
5. Cracks in walls, or bowing of walls
6. Cracks in the floor, floor tiles, or the foundation
7. Doors and windows that will not open or close properly
8. Visible separation of window or door from frame, including garage doors
9. Spaces between walls and ceiling or floor
10. Walls rotating (moving at all)

Tip:

One good technique to test for a buckled wall is to stand next to the basement wall, with your face resting against the wall. Then, look straight along the wall to see if there is any bulging. This photo is an extreme example, but often using the technique just described, you will be able to see much more subtle bowing in basement walls.

Porch Railing Issue Example

Removing a wall, or any portion of a foundation or support system, will wreak havoc in a house. In the first photo, you can see that the railing is pulling out of the brick post.

Figure 1.7: Railing in Brick Post

In this next photo, you can see that the railing has been sheared off.

Figure 1.8: Sheared Railing

Finally, here's the culprit: The owner decided to remove a supporting wall under the porch. This space is a root cellar, which was accessed from the main basement area via a pass door. Evidently, the owner wanted outside access under the porch to store items, so he removed a portion of the wall under the porch.

Figure 1.9: Missing Support

Discussion Point 1.1

What building envelope or foundation issues have you seen in houses?

_____

_____

_____

_____

_____

Common Practices to Avoid Foundation Issues

Common practices in new construction to avoid foundation issues include:

1. A water resistant tar is applied to the block below grade.

2. A trench with perforated pipe is backfilled with 2B Limestone to carry water around and away from the foundation. This is essentially an exterior French drain.

3. Drainage around foundations that coincides with proper gutters and downspouts protect the envelope. As builders say, "You can't stop water; you can only divert it."

Chapter Summary

1. The function of the building envelope is to protect the inhabitants from weather, keep them comfortable and safe, and provide elements needed to live in the house.

2. A building can be breached in many ways, including water, air, mold, insects, and animal infestation.

3. All properties are built on foundations, which rest on footers.

4. In older homes, posts (Lally columns) were used without footers.

5. Foundations can be formed using various materials such as stone, wood, poured concrete, concrete block, or pre-cast concrete.

6. Different types of soil require different construction techniques and safeguards.

7. Water and soils don't necessarily mix well. Hydrostatic pressure can collapse walls. Eroding limestone can cause sinkholes.

8. Visual signs of foundation issues include separation of walls, cracks, bowing, uneven floors, windows/doors that will not open/close properly, and spaces between walls and ceiling or floor.

Chapter Quiz

1. *Which of the following is NOT an area where a building envelope breach can occur?*

   a. basement
   b. doors and windows
   c. footer
   d. roof

2. *Which statement about foundations is TRUE?*

   a. All foundations require poured concrete footers.
   b. Most foundations today are poured concrete footers.
   c. Very old foundations are poured concrete footers.
   d. Wood foundations are the most common type of foundation.

3. *Which statement about a footer is TRUE?*

   a. It is always placed about 12" below the top of the soil.
   b. It is made of wood in today's construction.
   c. It is the same width as the wall built on top of it.
   d. It is wider than the wall it supports.

4. *Which type of foundation is placed on compacted gravel?*

   a. concrete block foundation
   b. laid stone foundation
   c. pre-cast foundation
   d. wood foundation

5. *A foundation created onsite by using a form is a*

   a. concrete block foundation.
   b. monolithic slab.
   c. poured concrete foundation.
   d. pre-cast foundation.

6. *Which type of termite is found in virtually all U.S. states?*

   a. dampwood
   b. drywood
   c. formosan
   d. subterranean

7. *Which state does NOT have any kind of termites?*

   a. Alabama
   b. Alaska
   c. Hawaii
   d. Maine

8. *When inspecting a house, standing close to the basement wall and looking straight ahead is a way to determine if there is*

   a. bowing in foundation walls.
   b. moisture in the house.
   c. radon in the house.
   d. termite infestation in the house.

9. *A component of soil that can cause sinkholes is*

   a. granite.
   b. limestone.
   c. marble.
   d. shale.

10. *Fill refers to*

    a. clay added to soil.
    b. rock added to soil.
    c. using the soil dug for the foundation to fill in holes in the yard.
    d. using soil or other materials to level a site or bring it up to a certain level.

11. *Which is a type of post used to help hold up a house?*

    a. Lally column
    b. Lateral post
    c. Lilly column
    d Load post

Chapter 2:
Types of Construction and Exterior Walls

Introduction

In this chapter, we will discuss types of construction and exterior wall materials used in residential construction. There are a number of building techniques, both new and old, found in the United States, and some methods of building and exterior materials are more commonly found in some areas than in others. As the country was settled and permanent structures were built, people used whatever materials were found in their area. Today, one of the trends in green building is to use materials that come from a 70-mile radius of the house, to conserve energy used to transport exotic materials long distances.

Objectives

After completing this chapter, students will be able to:

- Identify types of construction techniques.
- Classify houses by the type of construction.
- Identify exterior materials used on houses.

Adobe Among the earliest of building materials where soil, dung or straw, and water are made into bricks.

Aluminum In construction, a siding material made from aluminum that has a baked-on enamel finish.

Asbestos In construction, a building material made from a hardened mixture of asbestos, Portland cement, and water; used in siding and shingles.

Balloon Framing A technique of framing where the long vertical pieces (studs) are installed in a continuous piece from foundation to roof line.

Beam A long piece of timber (or metal) that spans an opening or part of a building, and provides support to a roof or floor above it. Beams are installed horizontally.

Brick A building material used either as a veneer, or in double or triple brick construction.

Composition Asphalt A siding material made of colored granules glued to asphalt; this material was widely used from the 1930s through the 1950s.

Concrete or Cement Siding A durable siding material made of concrete fibers and other materials.

Masonite® A brand name for hardboard siding made by mixing wood chips with glue.

(continued on page 15)

Key Terms

Exterior Walls

Once the foundation is in place, whether a slab, a crawl space, or a full basement, the next step is building exterior walls. The majority of walls are frame, with siding over the framing; however, there are other options (e.g., solid masonry, straw bale, stone).

Wood

Wood houses include frame houses, post and beam houses, and log cabins. On many frame dwellings, the wood is the centerpiece of the exterior, and may be stained, as opposite to painted, to allow the beauty of the wood to show through.

Much of the United States, when settled, had virgin forests, which made building frame houses not only practical, but gave the settlers something to do with the forests they cleared to make farmland. For example, houses located in Williamsport, Pennsylvania, once known as "the Lumber Capital of the World," which date from the 19th century have an amazing amount of wood, and quality wood in them. It is not unusual, along "Millionaire's Row" in Williamsport, to see a basement where the floor joists are true 2 x 12s, 12" on center, and made of solid oak!

Special Types of Wood Houses

Some types of wood houses found today include the following:

- **Double Plank:** These houses were constructed in areas with a plentiful wood supply, with many of them as Pennsylvania farmhouses. They have planks that run vertically and horizontally, and the lath and plaster is applied directly to the interior plank. These houses lack any cavity for insulation or wiring, so remodeling them can be challenging.

- **Log:** These are homes constructed of logs. They can be found across the United States. Log homes are not maintenance free; some of the issues include insect infestation and shrinkage of the logs over time. Most log homes have a wood interior, often yellow pine, which has a varnish or polyurethane finish. These interior solid wood paneled walls will change color due to light exposure, so when one owner moves, the new owner may be frustrated to find that it is clear where pictures were hung and where large pieces of furniture stood. Here's an image of a log home.

Figure 2.1: Log Home
Photo courtesy of Melanie J. McLane

- **Log Veneer:** This has been developed as a less expensive home; it offers the 'log look' for less money, and the interior is often drywall. The log veneer can be treated with chemicals to prevent infestation.

- **Post and Beam:** These homes, which are relatively rare, are constructed using post and beam construction methods (much like what is used in barn construction). Rather than use studs in the side walls, post and beam uses posts that carry horizontal beams on which joists are supported.

  This method allows for fewer bearing partitions and, therefore, uses less material. Purists will actually use pegs, as opposed to nails, to construct them. Some Amish farmers still construct barns this way.

- **Cedar:** These are wood frame homes that are popular among buyers who like the look of cedar siding or shakes. They are not maintenance free and may require staining. However, in New England, these homes are often not painted or stained, but allowed to weather to a silvery grey. Cedar shakes come in a variety of shapes and sizes.

House Framing

Prior to the 1950s, most frame houses built in the United States used **balloon framing**. In balloon framing, *the long pieces go from the foundation to the attic, and the floors are added later.* Since the 1950s, most houses in the United States use **platform framing**. In platform framing, the *first floor is built on top of the foundation, up to the second floor, where another platform (floor) is added, and then the house is continued upward from there.* The walls are anchored to the foundation, and the roof system is anchored to the side walls.

Masonry A general term referring to concrete, concrete block, brick, and stucco construction.

Platform Framing A technique of framing where a platform is built over the basement or crawl space, and then studs are extended up to the next level, where another platform is built; finally studs are extended to the roof line.

Post A long piece of timber or metal is installed vertically that supplies support for horizontal pieces, such as beams.

Stone A building material used for walls and foundations in old houses; imitation or engineered stone siding is available today.

Straw Bale In construction, a building method using bales of straw. Walls constructed of straw bales have a stucco-like finish installed over them as an exterior finish.

Stucco A building material made of aggregates, a binder, and water, which is applied over mesh, usually on top of masonry or wood.

Vinyl A durable siding material that comes in many colors, and is relatively inexpensive. Continues to be popular in home construction today.

Weep Holes Holes deliberately made in brick veneer applications to carry moisture away from the building and to equalize air pressure.

Key Terms

Platform Framing

Fire Stop →

Figure 2.2: Platform Framing

√ **Note:** In hurricane prone areas, specific building codes must be followed to ensure that the house, or a portion of it, will not lift off the foundation and become airborne.

House Siding

When wood was plentiful, the sheathing placed on top of the framing, and under the siding, was strips of solid wood, often placed diagonally. Today, the sheathing placed under any siding is usually a particle board material.

Many wood frame houses are subsequently covered with other kinds of siding, including:

- Asbestos
- Adobe
- Composition asphalt
- Imitation stone veneer
- Steel siding
- Masonite® siding

- Aluminum
- Vinyl
- Brick and brick veneer
- Stucco, including synthetic stucco, such as Dryvit®
- Concrete siding

What all of these sidings and finishes offer homeowners is the promise of less maintenance.

Asbestos

Asbestos siding was used from the 1920s through the 1980s, in the U.S. and Canada. At that time, the carcinogenic properties of asbestos were not known; the product was durable, a natural insulator, fireproof, and widely used. Asbestos was added to Portland cement, and the product was pressed into pieces of siding. It held paint well, and offered some degree of fire protection and insulation. Asbestos siding was made to look like cedar shakes; some of the siding had a wood grain pattern on it, to make it look like wood.

Here is a photo of asbestos siding:

Figure 2.3: Asbestos Siding
Photo courtesy of Melanie J. McLane

Some asbestos siding, like that pictured, had dye added to the Portland cement mixture, so the color went all the way through the product (much like inlaid linoleum). Although it didn't require painting, some homeowners painted it.

Most of the health risks associated with asbestos were in the factories where the products were manufactured, since the air was full of asbestos fibers. Asbestos siding as you see it today is generally not a health hazard, as asbestos needs to be friable to do harm, which means it can be crumbled when pressure is applied.

We'll discuss some of the other uses of asbestos in a future chapter on environmental issues.

Adobe

Adobe is one of the oldest materials used for construction and is found all over the world.

- It is a composite material made of earth, water, and organic materials such as straw or dung.

- The earth portion contains clay, sand, and silt.

- The straw works as a binding material, holding it together and allowing the brick to dry evenly.

Figure 2.4: Adobe House
Photo courtesy of Pam Bishop

Today, builders add emulsified asphalt or Portland cement to adobe. Adobe is found worldwide; it is quite commonly found in the American South West.

Composition Asphalt

Composition asphalt is the material many roofs are made of and was also used for siding. The product came out around the 1930s and was used extensively through the 1950s. Here's a picture of composition asphalt siding.

Figure 2.5: Composition Asphalt Siding
Photo courtesy of Melanie J. McLane

- Colored mineral granules were bonded to a wood product base with asphalt.
- Composition asphalt came in a variety of colors and styles, with patterns such as brick and stone.
- The sheets were rigid when installed.
- When composition asphalt wears out, the granules fall off and the black asphalt behind the granules shows; leaving a very unattractive exterior.

Imitation Stone Veneer

Historic stone veneers are known by brand names such as Perma-Stone, Formstone, Rostone, and others. The popularity of Formstone in Baltimore can be traced to Albert Knight, a native of the city, who patented it in 1937 for his Lasting Products Company. The City of Baltimore is famous for many buildings covered with Formstone, both residential and commercial, including churches, municipal buildings, etc. Here is a photo of one of the historic products.

Figure 2.6: Old Stone Veneer
Photo courtesy of Melanie J. McLane

Today, imitation stone veneer is making a comeback with newer versions that are authentic in appearance. This photo is of a house built in the early 1990s, with a 'stone' front added around 2010. As you can see, this is a rather upscale house, and the look is very appealing.

Figure 2.7: New Stone Veneer
Photo courtesy of Melanie J. McLane

Steel Siding

Steel siding can still be found, although because of the expense and weight, most owners gravitate towards vinyl or aluminum. Early steel siding dented very easily.

Masonite (Hardboard) Siding

Masonite® is actually a brand name, commonly used to refer to any siding fiberboard or hardboard siding. Steam heat and pressure combine to make the boards dense, with a smooth finish. It has long been popular because of the cost, which is less than vinyl, solid wood, or cement. It looks very much like wood and aluminum siding when viewed from the street. However, if it is not installed correctly, or maintained properly, it will rot. Here's a photo of a house with Masonite® siding.

Figure 2.8: Fiberboard Siding
Photo courtesy of Melanie J. McLane

Aluminum Siding

Aluminum siding was invented in 1947 by Jerome Kaufman, who observed how well paint adhered to aluminum planes during World War II. Although most people installed it to get away from having to paint, this siding can be painted; and often if it is not, it develops a chalky finish. This product is still sold today, although more buyers today gravitate toward vinyl or concrete (cement) siding.

Masonry

Masonry houses are made of concrete block, with or without a veneer of brick or stucco. In this photo, owners installed vinyl siding over a concrete block wall in a masonry house.

Figure 2.9: Vinyl Siding Over Concrete
Photo courtesy of Melanie J. McLane

Brick

Solid masonry homes with bricks are built with double and triple brick construction.

- A double brick house is constructed using two layers of brick, then usually lath and plaster on top. This is a photo of a double brick house.

Figure 2.10: Double Brick House
Photo courtesy of Melanie J. McLane

- Triple brick homes are usually older, and are constructed using three layers of brick with plaster installed directly over the brick. Triple brick houses, like double plank houses, do not have a cavity for insulation and wiring. This is the exterior of a triple brick house.

Figure 2.11: Triple Brick House
Photo courtesy of Melanie J. McLane

Here is a photo of an interior view of a wall, showing how the interior walls are also brick. This is the staircase to the attic.

Figure 2.12: Interior Wall of Triple Brick House
Photo courtesy of Melanie J. McLane

Brick Veneer

Brick veneer is a *thin brick that can be applied to virtually any existing interior or exterior wall.*

- It is installed over frame (most common) or masonry.
- There is a deliberate gap for air between the framing and the brick.
- Sheathing paper is installed over the framing to keep moisture out.
- There is a "brick lug" in which the brick rests on.
- Brick veneer has weep holes to allow water to drain out and to equalize air pressure.

Here is an image of a brick veneer house, built in 1951.

Figure 2.13: Brick Veneer House
Photo courtesy of Melanie J. McLane

Stone

Stone houses can be either stone veneer or solid stone. The width of the walls is about 18", and the stone is used from foundation to attic.

The house pictured here dates from the late 1700s and is solid stone. This home proved exceptionally challenging for the owner to have rewired.

Figure 2.14: Stone House; Photo courtesy of Melanie J. McLane

Stucco

Stucco is a type of finishing plaster used on the exterior of buildings, installed over wood sheathing. There is a **weep screed**, which is *a piece of metal at the base of the wall,* designed to take water away from the wall.

Stucco is typically installed in three coats:

1. A waterproof building paper is installed on top of the sheathing, followed by a metal lath or welded wire lath. This holds the first coat of stucco, known as the "scratch coat."

2. The next coat is known as the "brown coat."

3. The final coat is the "finish coat."

As you can see from this photo of a home in California, the finish coat can be very smooth.

Figure 2.15: Newer Stucco House
Photo courtesy of Karen Bloem-Peyton

Stucco homes are common in Florida and the southwest, but can be found in many places in the United States. This image is of an older stucco house.

Figure 2.16: Older Stucco House; Photo courtesy of Karen Bloem-Peyton

EIFS Systems

Although similar in appearance but a different composition than stucco, EIFS (exterior insulation and finishing systems) are products that provide excellent insulation, waterproofing, and if installed correctly, are maintenance free; the most commonly known is "Dryvit®."

Here is a picture of a triple brick house *before* it was covered with Dryvit®.

Figure 2.17: House Before Dryvit®; Photo courtesy of Melanie J. McLane

This photo shows the home *after* Dryvit® was installed. Note that the use of Dryvit® allowed the creation of **quoins**, which are *block or brickwork on the corners of a building*.

Figure 2.18: House After Dryvit®
Photo courtesy of Melanie J. McLane

Vinyl

Vinyl is a popular siding material because it is maintenance free, and of all the types of siding available, is one of the least expensive. It is fairly ubiquitous in new construction, and is often a "fix up" for an older home, like this one.

Figure 2.19: Vinyl Siding
Photo courtesy of Melanie J. McLane

Metal

Early metal homes, some of which are still around, include:

- **National Homes** (identified by a metal sign outlining the home's care instructions and serial number that was screwed into the wall of the small laundry area off the kitchen)

- **Lustron Homes** (prefabricated enameled steel houses).

These homes are a part of the American landscape, and were sold by two retail giants: Sears, Roebuck, & Co. and Montgomery Ward.

Metal houses are still being built today, like this one in Texas. This house has a metal roof and is on a slab, which is typical for the area. Inside, the ceiling is tongue and grove pine, and the floors are a porcelain wood-look tile.

Figure 2.20: Metal Siding; Photo courtesy of Alisa McKeel Willson

National Homes

National Homes Corporation was founded in 1940, and built houses through the early 1970s. These homes were typically placed on a slab, with about five (5) floor plans. Many are quite small (less than 800 square feet). These homes were part of the post WWII building boom.

- Used a stressed-skin panelized method of construction.
- The houses were prefabricated.
- The floor framing was steel.
- The framing studs were 2 x 3, and 3/8 inch waterproof plywood was mounted on to these studs.
- Doors and windows were pre-installed.

Lustron Houses

Lustron houses were made of prefabricated porcelain enameled steel. Lustron Corporation was only in business from 1948 to 1950, when bankruptcy forced them out of business.

- The panels were produced at the factory, then shipped for assembly on site.
- The colors were generally pastels: yellow, light green, pink, blue and grey.
- Their unique design made it possible to hang pictures using magnets, as both sides of the metal panels were exposed.

Chapter Summary

1. Construction of wood houses include double plank, log, log veneer, post and beam, and cedar.

2. Wood framing for houses use balloon framing (prior to 1950s) or platform framing (after the 1950s).

3. Siding for homes include asbestos, adobe, composition asphalt, imitation stone veneer, steel, Masonite, aluminum, masonry (block, brick, brick veneer, stone, or stucco), EIFS, vinyl, and metal.

4. National Homes Corporation built steel framed houses in the 1940s through 1970s.

5. Lustron Corporation built prefabricated porcelain enameled steel houses in the post-WWII era, from 1948 to 1950.

Chapter Quiz

1. *Which is NOT an attribute of brick building material used in houses?*

   a. composite
   b. double brick
   c. triple brick
   d. veneer

2. *A construction technique that uses long pieces of wood running vertically and horizontally is known as*

   a. balloon framing.
   b. double plank house.
   c. log construction.
   d. platform framing.

3. *Stucco is normally applied in*

   a. one coat.
   b. two coats.
   c. three coats.
   d. four coats.

4. *Which type of construction is most commonly used for framing houses today?*

   a. balloon framing
   b. double plank
   c. platform framing
   d. post and beam

5. *For existing homes, _____ was (were) commonly installed as upgraded siding to reduce home maintenance.*

   a. aluminum
   b. brick
   c. cedar shakes
   d. stucco

6. *_____ has mineral granules affixed to it.*

   a. Asbestos
   b. Composition asphalt
   c. Steel
   d. Stucco

7. *Which of the following siding products is also known as hardboard?*

   a. asbestos
   b. cedar shakes
   c. Masonite®
   d. stucco

8. *EIFS, which is the technical name for the brand name Dryvit©, stands for*

   a. External Imitation and Framing System
   b. Exterior Inclusive Finishing Set Up
   c. External Insulation and Finish System
   d. Extra Insulation for Stucco

9. *All of these types of construction might cause difficulty with wiring and insulation because of the lack of a cavity in the walls EXCEPT*

   a. double plank.
   b. masonry.
   c. solid stone.
   d. triple brick.

10. *Which of these building materials is the oldest?*

    a. adobe
    b. aluminum
    c. asbestos
    d. steel

Chapter 3:
Roofing

Introduction

In this chapter, we will examine roofing styles and roofing materials, as well as problems with roofs. We will also have a brief discussion on rain gutters and downspouts.

Objectives

After completing this chapter, students will be able to:

- Identify common roof styles and roofing terms.
- Recognize basic roofing components.
- Describe common roofing materials, including the advantages and problems associated with them.
- Identify types of gutters and downspouts.

Asbestos A building material commonly found in siding, during the era from 1930's through 1980's.

Clay Tile A roofing tile of fired earthenware clay.

Composition Asphalt Siding A siding material that consists of colored granules glued to asphalt; this material was widely used from the 1930s through the 1950s.

Fiberglass Shingles A roofing product made the same way as asphalt shingles, except that the base is made of fiberglass.

Flat Roof A roof with a minimal pitch that allows water to drain off.

Gabel A roof having a single slope on each side of a central ridge and a gable at one or both ends; most common style of roof.

Gambrel Roof A roof that has two pitches on each side (change in slope partway up the roof); often seen on barns.

Hip Roof A roof that has four slopes, with two that are shorter and triangular.

Joists Long beams of wood or steel that span the piers of a foundation or the load bearing walls of a roof.

Metal Roof A roofing system made from metal panels or pieces.

Mansard Roof A roof that has two distinct slopes with the lower one steeper than the upper one, often with a flat roof on top.

Oriented Strand Board (OSB) An engineered wood particle board that is glued and compressed.

Rafters Sloped support beams that follow the pitch of the roof and serve to hold the outer roof covering.

(continued on page 29)

Function of Roofs

The functions of a roof are to keep the elements out of the house and provide adequate ventilation. If proper ventilation is not in place, problems can occur, including:

- **Condensation** – Too much moisture can cause mold growth on rafters and soaking of insulation, reducing its efficiency.
- **Roofing issues** – Excessive attic heat can cause premature aging of shingles and warping or cracking of wood framing.
- **Poor air quality** – Improper circulation may lead to asthma or other breathing problems.
- **Higher electricity costs** – Poor air flow can cause air conditioner systems to run excessively.

A common form of roof ventilation is a **ridge vent**, which is *a vent running horizontally along the ridge, at the highest point of the roof where two or more planes come together*. Ridge vents work with vented **soffits** to create air flow underneath the sheathing. Thus, building codes today do *not* allow for insulation of soffits.

Roof Styles

Roof styles vary but there are some common styles built on most homes, as shown in this diagram.

COMPARISON OF ROOF STYLES		
Type	**Pros**	**Cons**
Gable	• Low cost • Installs easily • Rain and snow slides off easily • More attic space and ventilation • High ceiling space	• Prone to damage in high winds or tornados
Hip	• Sturdy and durable • Rain and Snow slides off easily • Less vulnerable to wind damage • Can be incorporated into an existing structure • High ceiling space	• Expensive • Complex to construct • Requires eaves and gutters on all four sides • Seams may allow for rain leakage • Hard to ventilate
Mansard	• Provides extra living space in attic or loft • Can be built on for an additional space	• Expensive • Complex to construct • Prone to leakage in areas with high rain and snow • Requires frequent maintenance
Gambrel	• Low cost • Installs easily • Provides extra living space in attic or loft • Good for outdoor buildings	• Prone to damage in high winds, tornados, or heavy snowfall • Requires frequent maintenance
Saltbox	• Sturdy and durable • Rain and snow slides off easily • Additional living space in front	• Expensive • Complex to construct • Limited attic space • Some rooms have slanted ceilings
Flat	• Low cost • Installs easily • Roof can be used for a patio, garden, or other living area	• Prone to leakage in areas with high rain and snowfall • Requires frequent maintenance
Shed	• Low cost • Installs easily • Rain and snow slides off easily	• Prone to damage in high winds or tornados

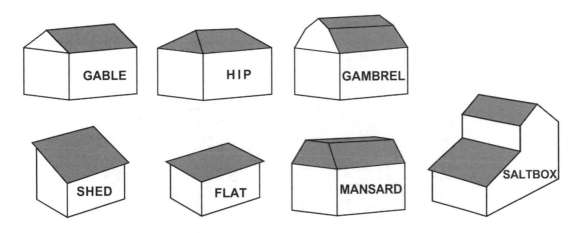

Figure 3.1 Common Roof Styles

Roof Pitch

Determining **roof pitch**, which is *a numerical measure of the steepness of a roof,* is actually pretty simple; in fact, most people in the construction trades and many expert real estate people can determine the pitch by 'eyeballing' the roof.

- Roof pitch is determined by how many inches of incline there are to each 12 inches (one foot) of horizontal span (or run), expressed as a ratio. For example, 3:12 means the roof rises 3 inches for every 12" of run.

- The higher the first number, the steeper the roof, so if a builder says "It's a 5:12 roof," it is steeper than a 4:12 roof.

- Steeper roofs are found in areas likely to get a heavy snow load, like New England and the Northern United States.

Ridge Beam A structural member at the top of the roof used to support the ends of the rafters at the ridge.

Ridge Vent A vent running horizontally along the ridge, at the highest point of the roof where two or more planes come together.

Rise The distance from the attic floor to the peak of the roof.

Roof Pitch A numerical measure of the steepness of a roof. The roof's vertical rise is divided by the horizontal span (or run), expressed as a ratio of the number of inches of incline per each 12 inches, with the rise followed by the run (e.g., 3:12).

Roof Trusses A framework of rafters, posts, and beams that forms the support for a roof.

Run The distance from the center to the edge of the roof. The runs added together equal the span.

Saltbox Roof A roof that is shorter in the front and slopes down in the back; the front is two stories and the back is one story.

Sheathing A layer of boards or other wood or fiber materials applied to the outer studs, joists, and rafters to strengthen the structure and serve as a base for exterior weatherproof covering.

Shed Roof A flat roof that slopes in one direction; often used on porch roofs, or additions to houses.

Slate Roof A roof made of slate layers, tiles, or plates.

Soffit The finished underside of the overhanging edge of a roof.

Span The entire length from one side of a building to the other.

Key Terms

Rafters and Beams

Rafters are *the sloped support beams that follow the pitch of the roof and serve to hold the outer roof covering*. The top of the rafters are fastened to the **ridge beam**, which *supports the ends of the rafters*. **Collar beams (collar ties)**, *the horizontal beams between two rafters*, are essential when additional weight is on the roof. They prevent the walls from being pushed outward.

Figure 3.2: Rafters and Beams

Roof Joists and Trusses

Roof joists and trusses form the structure of the roof. **Roof joists** are *long beams of wood or steel that supports the load bearing walls of a roof*. **Trusses** are *the framework of rafters, posts, and beams that forms the support for a roof*. Trusses are constructed to form the particular roof pitch and roof style of the house, as you can see in figure 3.3.

√ **Note:** Today, most roof joists and trusses are pre-made off site, then delivered, and installed at the construction site.

Sheathing

After the trusses are installed, sheathing is installed. **Sheathing** is *a layer of boards or other wood or fiber materials applied to the outer studs, joists, and rafters to strengthen the structure and serve as a base for exterior weatherproof covering*). Plywood used to be the most common sheathing material, but **OSB (oriented strand board)**, *an engineered product made of particles of wood particularly suitable for load-bearing applications in construction*, has surpassed it, mainly because of cost. Figure 3.4 shows both roof and wall sheathing made of OSB.

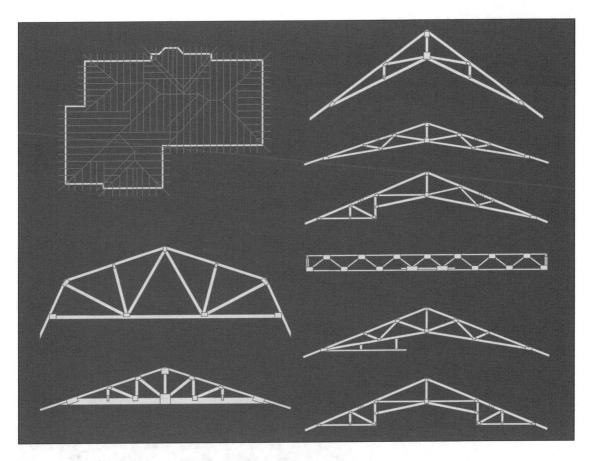

Figure 3.3: Roof Trusses

Figure 3.4: OSB Sheathing

Roofing Materials

Now, let's examine common types of roofing materials you are likely to see.

Composition Asphalt

In the U.S., asphalt roofing was introduced circa 1901 and by the 1930s, was a popular roofing material. **Composition asphalt** is *a very common type of roofing material composed of a base material of felt with asphalt coating, followed by granules.* Asphalt roofing is installed over sheathing, followed by a layer of tar paper, and then the asphalt shingles. Most composition asphalt roofs have life spans between 15 to as many as 40 years. The longer the roof is expected to last, the more expensive it will be.

When asphalt shingles wear out, several things happen:

- The granules come off the shingles.
- The black asphalt underneath is exposed.
- The shingles curl up.

In this photo, there has been leaking at the flashing where the two roofs meet, which someone has patched with tar. This is a temporary fix, not a permanent one.

Figure 3.5: Worn Composition Asphalt Roof

Fiberglass

Fiberglass roofing is made the same way as asphalt shingles, except for the base—rather than an organic product, such as felt, or even in the early 20th century, cotton, is *a base of fiberglass.*

Slate

Slate roofs are made of a very thin slice of slate rock.

The slate pieces are cut into various shapes and sizes and can be found in different colors. The weight of a slate roof is tremendous—it is estimated at about 8 to 10 pounds per square inch. Slate roofing is still available today, although it is very pricey. Slate roofs, if maintained, last for decades. Slates do come loose and fall off; repair work should be done by an experienced slate roof repair company. This image is of a slate roof that dates from circa 1890, and is located in Williamsport, PA. Note that old slate roofs do not have sheathing underneath them.

Figure 3.6: Slate Roof

Asbestos

In the U.S., asbestos roofing was introduced around 1906. Asbestos roofing was marketed to homeowners with the lure of being fireproof. For example, an early advertisement from Johns Manville Company showed a house destroyed by fire, with an intact roof, and the caption "The roof didn't burn!" Asbestos shingles were viewed as a miracle building material—fireproof, durable, and a natural insulator. Because of this, you will still see them today in many parts of the United States. This roof can be identified as asbestos from the shingle pattern. Note the small black holes in this roof; it is very likely this roof endured a hail storm that caused the small holes.

Figure 3.7: Asbestos Roof

Unfortunately, asbestos was discovered to be carcinogenic. It is dangerous when **friable**, which is *when the particles of asbestos become dry, brittle, and can be pulverized by hand pressure.* When the particles are airborne, they can lodge in a person's lungs and become a serious health hazard, leading to **mesothelioma**, which is *a rare, asbestos-related cancer that forms on the thin protective tissues that cover the lungs and abdomen.* The people exposed to the greatest risk from asbestos were workers in the factories where asbestos was present.

Metal

Metal roofs have been around for a long time and are enjoying a renaissance. Once primarily made of a dull, natural color, metal roofs today come in a variety of colors, and some imitate the look of other building materials, such as tile. Most of them are made of steel.

Figure 3.8: (left) Old Metal Roof and (right) New Metal Roof

Some homeowners install metal roofing directly over existing roofing. There are pros and cons to this, but one source states that by installing metal roofs directly over existing shingles, the noise factor of the steel (metal) roof is reduced considerably.

Metal roofs can have:

- Conventional panels, which are screwed with neoprene washers exposed, or
- A standing seam with no exposed fasteners, which is more expensive.

Metal roofs do not require sheathing and last a very long time. However, a vapor barrier is recommended to prevent condensation and rotting.

Tile

Clay is the oldest known roofing material; it can be traced to both China and the Middle East 10,000 years BC. Clay tiles have been known to last for well over 100 years, making them an extremely durable product. And like slate, their durability means that they are costly. Some companies salvage old roof tiles to be used again.

Figure 3.9: Clay Roof

In many parts of the United States, primarily the South and West, tile roofs are common. These roofs are made of clay tile or concrete. The clay tile roofs have the distinctive reddish color; the concrete products can be made in a variety of colors.

Clay roofs are not light weight; like slate, they are heavy. Roofing squares are 100 square feet (an area 10 x 10), and it is estimated that tile roofs can weigh between 580 to 1100 pounds per square.

Rolled Roofing

At the other end of the price spectrum is rolled roofing, which is probably the least expensive roofing material you will see. It is advertised by one major manufacturer as "the economical solution for any low pitched roof." Many builders regard it as a temporary use product. It is often seen on cabins, camps, and farm outbuildings.

Figure 3.10: Rolled Roof

- Rolled roofing is made of the same materials as asphalt shingles, but made in a wide width (usually about 36"), and placed on a roll.
- It is rolled out onto the roofing surface, which is prepared sheathing.
- Roofing cement holds it in place.

√ **Note:** The width makes rolled roofing vulnerable to the contraction and expansion that occurs with temperature changes.

This is a photo of a cabin near Slate Run, PA. The roof is covered with rolled roofing.

Layering Roofing Materials

Most contractors do *not* recommend installing new shingles over old ones, for several reasons:

- More layers add extra weight to the roof.

- Many shingle manufacturers will not warrant their product if it is installed over existing shingles.

- At some point, all of the shingles will have to come off. The more layers there are, the more expensive this will be.

√ **Caution:** It is important to remember that the **FHA has a limit of three (3) layers of roofing**.

Gutters and Downspouts

The purpose of gutters and downspouts is to reroute water that falls on the roof away from the foundation. Modern contractors often bury lines of flexible plastic pipe in the yard to carry water away from the house.

Materials used for gutters and downspouts include the following:

- **Wood** was used to make rain gutters for centuries, and some purists restoring old homes today will still install wood gutters. They are not maintenance free, but do provide an authentic look.

- **Galvanized** gutters and downspouts were installed on older homes. These tend to rust over time.

- **Copper** gutters and downspouts are typically used on more expensive homes. You can recognize them from the distinctive blue-green color that develops as the copper oxidizes.

- **Aluminum** is the material used on most gutters and downspouts today. They are available in a wide array of colors.

Leaks

The primary problem with roofs is that they leak:

- Many times, a roof will leak in a valley (where two planes come together) or around the flashing on a chimney. Often, when you are inside a house, you can see signs of water damage around the flue, or chimney in the attic. This indicates a leak, either past or present.

- If you are in a house with a wet corner in the basement, look outside. A very high percentage of the time, the reason is a clogged gutter or missing downspout. Evidence of clogged gutters includes a line in the soil underneath the gutter, meaning that the water is overflowing the gutter and pouring onto the ground.

Here is a photo of an extreme example. In this case, the roof leaked, rotting the sheathing underneath, and the section collapsed, causing a large hole.

Figure 3.11: Leaking Roof

Discussion Point 3.1

Most everyone has seen the destruction that water entering a house can do. What water damages have you seen in houses?

_____

_____

_____

_____

Ice Dams

In some parts of the country (New England, for example), gutters are *not* installed as ice dams can form in the gutters. As a defense against ice dams, you will often see the lower portion of the roof covered with a different roofing material.

- Ice dams usually happen on a sunny, below freezing day on the upper part of a dark roof, when the roof temperature is above freezing, which causes the snow on the roof to melt.

- The melted snow runs down the roof until it hits a spot where the roof temperature is below freezing.

- Because both the lower part of the roof and the air are below freezing, the melted snow freezes and causes icicles that back up under the shingles, eventually causing leaks in the house.

Chapter Summary

1. Roofs keep elements out of the house and provide necessary ventilation.

2. Roof styles vary greatly, the most common being the gable roof. Other roof styles include flat, gambrel, hip, mansard, flat, shed, and saltbox.

3. Roof pitch is calculated by dividing the rise from the span, which is expressed as a ratio (e.g., 3:12).

4. Roofing materials include composition asphalt, fiberglass, asbestos, metal, tile, and rolled.

5. Rain gutters and downspouts are made of various material—wood was used for centuries, galvanized metal was used on many older homes, cooper is installed on more expensive homes, and aluminum is mostly used today.

6. Roofs can leak and wear out. Leaks are commonly found in a valley (where two planes meet) or around the flashing on a chimney.

7. Homes in certain parts of the country do not have gutters installed to prevent ice dams from forming.

Chapter Quiz

1. *Which roofing material has the shortest lifespan?*

   a. asbestos
   b. clay tile
   c. composition asphalt
   d. slate

2. *Which type of roofing material does NOT require sheathing underneath it?*

   a. asbestos shingles
   b. composition asphalt
   c. rolled roofing
   d. slate

3. *Which roofing material has been in use the longest time?*

   a. asbestos
   b. clay tile
   c. composition asphalt
   d. slate

4. *A roof with only two planes of equal size that meet at the ridge is a*

   a. gable roof.
   b. gambrel roof.
   c. mansard Roof.
   d. shed roof.

5. *A roof design associated with Victorian architecture is a*

   a. gable roof.
   b. gambrel roof.
   c. mansard roof.
   d. saltbox roof.

6. *Which type of roof has four sides and eaves on all four sides?*

   a gable
   b. gambrel
   c. hip
   d. mansard

7. *The type of roof most commonly seen on a porch or an addition is a*

   a. gable roof.
   b gambrel roof.
   c. mansard roof.
   d. shed roof.

8. *Which type of roofing is the least expensive and least likely to last?*

   a. clay tile
   b. composition asphalt
   c. rolled
   d. steel

9. *Layering shingles on top of shingles may*

   a. add life expectancy to the roof.
   b. make the eventual removal of shingles less expensive.
   c. make it easier to eventually replace the roof.
   d. void the manufacturer's warranty on the shingles.

10. *A point of entry for a leak on a roof is commonly the*

    a. flashing on a chimney.
    b. gable end.
    c. joists and rafters.
    d. section near the soffit.

11. *Which is the most common material used today in rain gutters and downspouts?*

    a. aluminum
    b. copper
    c. galvanized metal
    d. wood

12. *When restoring a historic house, an owner might choose gutters made of*

    a. aluminum.
    b. galvanized.
    c. wood.
    d. zinc.

13. *An ice dam is caused by*

    a. gutters being clogged with leaves.
    b. improper installation of rain gutters.
    c. melting snow on the upper part of the roof hitting a colder part of the roof and refreezing.
    d. temperatures above freezing on both the roof and in the air.

Chapter 4:
Interior Finishes, Doors, and Windows

Introduction

In this chapter, we will discuss the many types of interior finishes for walls, ceilings, and floors. We will also look at the materials used for exterior and interior doors. We will end this chapter by covering types of windows found in homes.

Objectives

After completing this chapter, students will be able to:

- Describe typical wall, ceiling, and floor coverings used in homes.
- Recall materials used for exterior doors.
- Identify styles of interior doors.
- Identify types of windows typically found in residential construction.

Awning Window A window hinged at the top that opens out from the building, commonly found in basements.

Blueboard A type of drywall with a distinctive blue paper covering on which specially formulated plaster is applied.

Casement Window A window hinged, usually on the side, that can open outward or inward.

Ceiling Tiles Tiles that are hung from a metal grid or installed directly onto a ceiling. Ceiling tiles are made of a variety of materials; some may contain asbestos.

Clerestory Window A window located high on a high wall, above eye level.

Double Hung Window A window where both the lower sash goes up and the upper sash goes down.

Drywall A building material made by putting a sheet of gypsum board between two sheets of heavy paper. Also called **Plasterboard**, **Wallboard**, or **Gypsum Board**.

Fenestration The arrangement of doors and windows in a house. For example, classic Colonial styles have even fenestration (center door with equal numbers of windows on both sides).

Fixed Window A window that does not move at all; often found as picture windows.

Gypsum A soft sulfate mineral, used in blackboard chalk and in plaster and drywall.

(continued on page 41)

Key Terms

Interior Construction

Once the house is under roof, the interior partitions are put in place. These delineate rooms, as well as closets, stairwells, and other areas.

- Rough-in plumbing is installed at this point.
- Wiring should be in place *before* drywall and insulation are added.
- Interior walls do not have to be insulated, but many people do so for a variety of reasons. The most common reasons are noise reduction and energy efficiency.
- In attached houses (like townhouses or condominiums), these walls not only need to be insulated, but be as fireproof as possible.

Figure 4.1: Interior Construction, Photo courtesy of Tim Tepes

Wall Finishes

At this point, some kind of finish will be put on the walls and the ceilings. The most commonly used finish today is **drywall**. Drywall has been the interior wall product of choice since the 1950s.

Drywall

There are several types of drywall, each with a specific use.

- **Moisture resistant** drywall is used in kitchens and bathrooms where the moisture content is likely to be high. The core of this drywall is impregnated with waterproofing materials, but the surface is "breathable." This type of drywall is often used as a base for ceramic tiles in a bathroom shower.

- **Foil backed** drywall has a silver foil-like layer on the side that goes against the studs. It is used in cold climates but not considered a good fit for moist areas or climates with high humidity.

Figure 4.2: Drywall, Photo courtesy of Melanie J. McLane

- **Fire-resistant (or Type X)** drywall should be installed between a garage and a house. In the case of a built-in garage where there is living space both adjacent to the garage and above the garage, there should be fire-resistant drywall on all surfaces that connect to the house. Within the past couple of years, building code has changed to require "mud" (the drywall adhesive) to be placed under the tape, and over the tape, for fire-resistant drywall (normal installation only calls for mud on top of the tape). One 5/8" layer of fire-resistant drywall is rated as one hour of fire proofing; two layers would offer two hours.

- **Abuse resistant** drywall is used in high traffic areas, such as hallways. It has a polystyrene layer bonded to the side that goes against the studs.

- **Soundproof** drywall is specially designed for use in walls and ceilings in apartments and condos.

- **Cement board** is not really drywall, but manufactured in a similar fashion and is often found near the drywall section in building supply stores. It has a very strong moisture-resistant base and is used underneath ceramic tiles on both walls and floors.

Drywall comes in a variety of thicknesses; most carpenters use 1/2" drywall on walls. For ceilings, 5/8" drywall is preferred, for a couple of reasons.

- The joists are 24" on center, so the span is wider, and the thicker, slightly heavier drywall is actually less likely to sag.

- Often after the drywall is installed in the ceiling, insulation is blown into the ceiling, which caused the 1/2" drywall to sag.

Key Terms

Hollow-core Door A door (usually interior) where sandwiched between a thin press-board or wood veneer exterior is a cardboard honeycomb. Hollow core doors can be flush or have raised panels.

Hopper Window A window similar to an awning window, except it is often hinged at the bottom and opens into the building; commonly found in basements.

Jalousie Window A window of slats of glass, moved with a crank; often seen on older storm doors, porch doors, and windows.

Lath Thin, flat strips of wood used to hold plaster to walls or ceilings.

Luan (or Lauan) Wood from a number of tropical southeast Asian trees, which varies in color from light yellow to reddish-brown or brown. Luan is used as an underlayment under carpeting and in the construction of hollow core doors. Also called **Philippine Mahogany**.

Muntins and Mullions The strips of wood (or other materials) separating panes of glass in a window. The muntins are vertical and the mullions are horizontal.

Paneling A building material that comes in panels in a variety of materials—from solid wood paneling to fiberboard paneling, and some laminated paneling that resembles wallpaper. The thickness, durability, and cost all vary.

Plaster A soft, thick mixture of lime or gypsum, sand, water, and sometimes hair or other fiber, applied when wet and dries in place. Also called **Horsehair Plaster**.

Single Hung Window A window where only the bottom part moves up and down and the upper part is fixed.

Sliding Window A window that slides from one side to the other to allow fresh air.

Storm Window A window installed to offer weather protection and more insulation.

Thermal Window A window that has two or more layers of glass, with an inert gas between the panes. The most commonly used gas is argon; more expensive windows use krypton gas.

Triple Track Storm and Screen Combination A window that contains two panes of glass (upper and lower), as well as a screen. During warm weather, the extra panes of glass can be slid up and the screen slid down, allowing fresh air to get into the house.

Drywall is typically both glued and screwed to the studs or joists. Because walls studs in modern construction are 16" on center, the drywall crew follows this and installs screws at 16" vertically (going up the studs) to match the screws that are already in place horizontally, from stud to stud.

√ **Note:** Nails were used to install drywall as late as the early 1990s. You may have seen a house where the drywall nails have "popped."

Plaster

A more durable wall surface is **plaster**; it is also more expensive. Plaster can be installed as a wet product over **blueboard**, which is a form of drywall that has a special blue paper covering.

Traditional horsehair plaster was applied over **lath**, which are *thin flat strips of wood*. If you are in an old house and in a stairway leading to the basement or attic, you can often see the lath with the plaster visible through it, because both sides of those walls were not finished.

For Example
When you are in an old house where the walls are plaster, thump on them with your hand—the feel and the sound are much different than thumping on a drywall finish.

Smooth finishes on drywall tend to be found on the east coast, and textured finishes, known as "orange peel" or "knockdown," are more likely to be found on the west coast.

Paneling

Another alternative to drywall is **paneling**, which comes in a large variety of materials and detailing. Paneling can be found in formal rooms as well as informal rooms. The basic base of most paneling today is plywood. Because plywood will expand and contract in response to temperature and moisture level changes, if it is not installed properly, it may warp, especially if installed below grade.

- Fiberboard paneling has patterns and designs. In bathrooms of older homes (circa 1940 through 1960), you may see this paneling, which is scored to look like tile or coated with a laminate surface. These surfaces resist moisture but are not waterproof.

- In mid-20th century homes, knotty pine paneling is often found in dens, kitchens (where it was also used for cabinets), and some living rooms.

- Today, paneling is made from a variety of materials including hardwoods and softwoods, as well as hardboard (one brand name of which is Masonite®).

- Paneling can also come from a variety of solid wood products including barn boards, which are taken from barns and repurposed as a wall finish.

- Paneling can be an inexpensive covering for crumbling plaster in older homes, where it is often installed over the plaster.

This picture is of a room with solid hickory paneling, circa 1960.

Figure 4.3: Hickory Paneling, Photo courtesy of Melanie J. McLane

Ceilings

Ceilings can be plaster, drywall, tile, suspended tile, or even paneling, which many in the real estate business have seen.

- **Tin** – In very old buildings, especially old retail buildings, tin ceilings were popular. Some people who renovate old houses will either find and restore a tin ceiling, or install one.

- **Ceiling Tile** – Some ceiling tiles are glued directly to an existing ceiling. Most ceiling tiles are made of mineral fiber and have noise reducing qualities.

- **Suspended Tile** – Other ceiling tiles are suspended in a metal grid. Suspended ceilings are commonly found in basements, where the suspension area hides plumbing and wiring. Also, some stately old homes have unfortunately been remodeled and had the ceilings lowered in the interest of energy savings. However, dropping what was a 12' ceiling to 8' in a room that has the proper proportions to have a 12' ceiling can make the very large room take on the aspect of a bowling alley. Some suspended ceiling tiles have asbestos in them.

- **Popcorn** – Another type of ceiling installed circa 1950 through 1980 was the 'popcorn' or 'cottage cheese' ceiling. Both names are descriptive of the texture of these ceilings, and they may contain asbestos. Some of these ceilings also had glitter applied to them. Many homeowners want to remove these ceilings; however, before doing so, they should verify whether or not asbestos is present.

- **Swirled** – Another method that was popular circa 1950 through 1970s (roughly) was swirled ceilings, where a design was swirled onto the surface using a wet plaster mix. Sometimes, if a house has radiant electric heat, a swirl pattern of a flower is an indication of that type of heat.

Figure 4.4: Popcorn Ceiling (left) and Swirled Ceiling (right)

Flooring

Floor covering is varied and also runs the gamut from very inexpensive to very pricey. Like other things in housing, styles go out and come back in. New kinds of floor coverings are being created every day.

Wood

In most old houses, the original floors in most rooms were wood floors. Homes from the 1700s to late 19th century often had wide plank floors typically made of pine, although any wood at hand was used, including oak, maple, walnut, and even chestnut. Chestnut wood in a house indicates pre-early 1900s, as most chestnut trees in the United States were destroyed by a chestnut blight in the early 1900s. Many wood floors were painted.

As exotic woods became available, parquet floors, which are *made of patterned wood blocks (solid or veneer) that are geometrical and angular in nature; e.g., squares, triangles, herringbone,* came into vogue. Be aware, when looking at a home with parquet floors that if the room was designed to have a large rug in the center, the wood underneath the rug may be very plain—or in the case of a newer home, the center may be only plywood.

As the narrow strip hardwood floors became popular, many homebuilders cut costs by continuing to use tongue and groove pine floors on the second floor and in the bedrooms. The public rooms had the showier floors; the private rooms had plainer floors, also often covered with carpet.

Hardwood floors are very much in vogue as of the time of this writing, and new techniques of finishing them make for such durable finishes that they are found in kitchens and bathrooms.

Linoleum

Linoleum was invented by an Englishman, Frederick Walton, and was patented in 1863 after experimenting with several ingredients. Linoleum contains linseed oil in a solidified state, known as linoxyn, pine rosin, ground cork dust, wood flour, and some mineral fillers. It was put on a backing of burlap or canvass. The dye was often added to the materials, which meant the color went all the way through.

- Inlaid linoleum is solid pieces of linoleum joined together.
- Cheaper linoleum had patterns printed on it and came in rolls.
- Some linoleum was created in rug sizes, such as 9 x 12, and designed to be put down over a wood floor.

Linoleum is still produced today, but most modern floors that are called "linoleum" are actually vinyl flooring.

Marmoleum®

Marmoleum® is a 21st century version of linoleum. It contains mostly natural products, contains no VOCs (Volatile Organic Chemicals), and is extremely durable. It is expensive, but considered a very 'green' building material.

Vinyl

Vinyl floor coverings were first introduced in Sweden in 1947. Vinyl flooring comes in tiles, or rolls where it can be cut to fit and seamed, if necessary. Up until the mid-1980s, many vinyl flooring materials contained asbestos. Vinyl flooring remains a popular and inexpensive choice for kitchens and baths in many homes.

Figure 4.5: Old Vinyl Flooring

Asphalt Tile

Asphalt tiles were introduced in the 1920s, and by the 1950s, were found in many American homes. These tiles were often found in basement rec rooms, because they could be installed directly on concrete floors and did not deteriorate when exposed to alkali that sometimes leaches out of damp concrete floors. These tiles also resisted fire and rot. Part of the reason they were fire resistant was that, like so many building products of the time, they contained asbestos.

Carpet

Wall-to-wall carpeting was *not* a 20th century invention—it actually dates from the late 18th century. Wall-to-wall carpeting is a fixture (permanently installed) whereas room rugs, in most places, are considered to be personal property. Most wall-to-wall carpeting requires an under pad, which is made of rubber, felt, or urethane. Some carpeting is designed to be installed without an under pad; it has a rubber back that is glued directly to the surface. This is more commonly found in bathrooms, kitchens, and basement rec rooms.

Carpeting runs the gamut from very cheap (e.g., indoor-outdoor carpeting) to very expensive. It is made of a variety of materials, including yarns, synthetic and real (e.g., wool); burlap; nylon; polyester; glue; and backing.

Back in the 1970s, covering hardwood floors with carpeting was popular. Carpeting can give a house a 'dated' look, from the color or the composition. Nothing says '1970' like green shag, for example. Carpeting remains popular, and as in earlier times when the expensive hardwood was put in the living room and the pine floor in the bedrooms, today's new construction will often have hardwood in the living areas and carpeting in the bedrooms.

Laminates

The first laminate flooring to appear in residential homes was Pergo©, invented by a Swedish Company, Perstorp, in 1977. It was marketed in the U.S. beginning in the early 1990s. Since then, many companies have begun manufacturing laminate flooring, which can look like wood, tile, slate, or just about anything. Some laminate flooring is not water resistant, and a leaking appliance can ruin it. As is true for all building products, the more durable the product, the more expensive it is.

Porcelain Planks

Porcelain plank flooring, which has a pattern and design like wood, is very durable and is showing up in both houses and commercial applications (e.g., hotels). It is more expensive than some laminates, vinyl, and carpet.

Cork

Cork floors are made from the ground bark of cork trees, which is then molded, baked, cut, and varnished. Cork floors offer a surface that 'gives,' making them a good choice for a room where people stand often, like a kitchen.

> √ **Note:** Cork floors that are decades old are likely to have changed color with exposure to sunlight, making the areas under rugs and furniture a completely different color than the rest of the floor.

Slate or Flagstone

Slate or flagstone can be found in foyers, and sometimes mudrooms and kitchens. Both are a natural stone product, and often sealed when used in the interior of a house. This flooring is very durable, but there is no 'give' when standing on it, so it can cause fatigue, or pain for persons with arthritis.

Ceramic Tile and Terra Cotta

Tile is found in foyers, kitchens, and baths, and in some parts of the country, throughout a house. It is very durable, but again, it is a very hard surface for standing on for any length of time.

Although ceramic tile is more common, some floors are terra cotta tile. Both are made with clay, and the finish on terra cotta is usually porous, requiring a glaze or a sealant to protect it from staining. Tile floors were all the rage in the late 1980s through early 1990s for kitchens, but now we see more hardwood used in kitchens.

Doors

Doors can date a house, although some may have been replaced in older homes. When walking through a house, note the kinds of exterior and interior doors. Notice if they fit properly into the frame. A door that won't fit into the frame can indicate a warped door or frame.

As construction materials got more expensive, builders used less expensive materials for doors. Solid wood doors gave way to hollow core doors; wood was replaced with fiberboard (like Masonite®). At the same time, consumers began to expect more energy efficiency, so old wooden exterior doors were replaced with insulated wood or metal doors.

Exterior Doors

Exterior doors come in a variety of materials—from fiberglass, glass, steel, wood, and combinations of those. Exterior doors should be either solid wood or insulated metal, or a combination of metal and glass, or wood and glass.

- **Entrance door** – Should be heavy, well insulated, and offer protection from both the elements and anyone trying to break in. Most builders will use solid doors on the front, sometimes with sidelight windows (side panels with glass panes in them), but use a half glass and steel door on the rear.

- **Pass door from the garage** – Should be solid, insulated steel; it needs to offer protection and be fireproof.

- **French doors** – Can be used as exterior or interior doors. In newer construction, French doors as exterior doors have been replaced with **sliding glass doors**, which were commonplace beginning in the 1960s and continuing through the 1980s.

- **Back door** – A back exterior door that opens outward, not inward, is probably a manufactured house. This is due to the building code for manufactured (mobile) homes.

√ **Note:** You will occasionally find **hollow core** exterior doors on post WWII houses which were mass produced cheaply. Hollow core doors are not insulated and do not offer much resistance to someone trying to break them down.

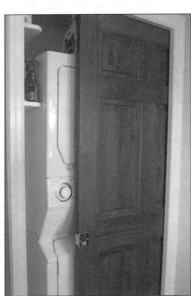

Figure 4.6: Hollow Core Exterior Door, Interior Flush Door, and Pocket Door

Interior Doors

Years ago when lumber was cheap, houses had solid wood doors, often with a panel design in them. When the price of lumber increased, interior doors were manufactured in a variety of styles and materials.

- **Six panel doors**, with a cross in the center, are often seen and labeled as "Colonial" in design, and hollow core doors sold today mimic this pattern. Some older houses have five horizontal panels in the door.

- **Hollow core doors** began to be used extensively post World War II. Hollow core doors have a honeycomb-like core of corrugated material, but transmit sound easily and can be damaged more easily than a solid wood door. However, they are lightweight and much cheaper than solid wood doors.

- **Flush doors** have no panels, just a smooth surface.

- **Louvers** are doors with slats of wood and are sometimes used for closets and other places where ventilation is needed.

- **Pocket doors** slide into a recess in the wall. This kind of door is very useful when you don't want the interference of a door opening into a room or area. Pocket doors have been around for many years. In older homes, pocket doors often were on the parlor, which was a formal room, not always used and heated, and therefore able to be shut off.

- **Bi-fold doors** have been around for centuries (the Romans had them), but in today's construction they are usually found on closet doors. Cheaper construction in the 1970s can be identified by metal bi-fold doors.

Windows

Glass window panes were once reserved for the wealthy, but by 1608, glass was being made in Jamestown, Virginia. At that time, only small panes could be made. By the early 1800s, the process for making smooth, rolled window glass was in use, allowing for larger windows.

For a long time, the standard was a single pane of glass in a window. **Storm windows** were introduced in the late 18th century, and were fairly common by the end of the 19th century. At that time, they were made of wood. Many of the old wooden storm windows still seen have a hinge attachment at the top. Although these windows were usually designed to be removed in the spring, and replaced with screens, the hinge at the top allowed the homeowner to prop the storm window open at the bottom using a stick, so that fresh air could get into the house. Wood frames for regular windows are still found today, although some wood frames are vinyl clad on the outside. The next innovation in storm windows was the **triple track storm and screen combination**. Ernest Camerino applied for a patent for the triple track storm and screen window combination on July 16, 1952; the patent (grant) was given to him on November 19, 1954.

Thermal windows were introduced by Andersen in 1962; the invention of thermal windows eliminated the need for storm windows. Originally just double-pane glass, thermal windows are now available in triple-pane glass. Additionally, today's thermal windows are **low-e**. Low-e means *low emissivity, which is how much a material can radiate energy.* **Low-e glass** *controls how much of which kind of light will enter the house.*

There are three kinds of light we are concerned with when discussing low-e:

- Ultraviolet (UV) light, which is the light that will fade carpet and upholstery;

- Visible light, which is the light you need to see what you are doing;

- Infrared light, which is transmitted as heat into a building.

The goal of low-e glass is to minimize UV and infrared light, while allowing visible light into the house.

Certain types of windows can help pinpoint the age and type of house:

- **Jalousie windows** were used in manufactured housing, extensively in the old single wide trailers.

- **Single- hung windows** are still used by many manufactured home builders today.

- **Double-hung windows** with separate storm windows are generally found up and into the early 1960s when thermal windows were introduced. Older thermal windows often are fogged because the seals have broken.

Some contractors claim that the seals are more likely to break on **casement windows**, due to the constant cranking in and out, than on double hung windows. However, many older homes now have replacement windows that solved a number of problems for homeowners: maintenance (painting and cleaning; most are vinyl clad on the outside and tilt in for easier washing), energy efficiency, and noise.

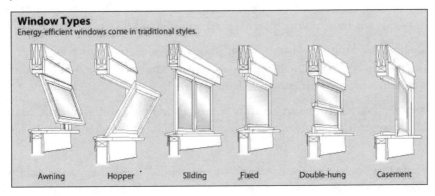

Figure 4.7: Types of Windows

Window Inspection

Note what kinds of windows are in a house and if they are functional. For example,

- Do the windows go up and down?

- Do they stay up by themselves? In older homes, where the windows use ropes, weights, and pulleys, a sure sign of a broken rope is a stick in the space between the main window and the storm window that is used to hold up the window.

- Are there storm windows?

- If an older house, have the windows been replaced?

- Does the owner know the U-value and whether or not they are low-e? U-value reflects the energy efficiency of the window.

Chapter Summary

1. Interior walls are finished using a variety of materials, most commonly drywall. Other finishes include plaster and paneling.

2. There are several types of drywall with each having a specific use: Moisture resistant, foil backed, fire resistant, abuse resistant, and soundproof. Although not considered drywall, cement board is a material used on walls and floors in moist areas.

3. Ceilings are built of plaster, drywall, tin, suspended tile, and paneling. Some older ceiling tiles and 'popcorn' or 'cottage cheese' ceilings contain asbestos. Swirled ceilings were often used in homes with radiant electric heat.

4. Various floor coverings are used in homes, including wood, linoleum, Marmoleum®, vinyl, asphalt tile, carpet, laminate, porcelain plank, cork, slate, flagstone, ceramic, and terra cotta.

5. Floor coverings go out of style and come back in. Wood floors are an example of this. Some homes have expensive wood flooring in the public rooms, such as the living room, and inexpensive wood in the private rooms upstairs and in bedrooms.

6. Exterior doors can be made of fiberglass, glass, steel, wood, or a combination of these. Exterior doors should be solid wood or insulated metal and can contain glass panels.

7. French doors can be used as either exterior or interior doors and are often replaced with sliding doors.

8. Interior doors come in different designs and materials. Six panel doors, flush doors, pocket doors, louvered doors, and bi-fold doors are common. Interior doors can be solid or hollow core.

9. Various types of windows can help pinpoint the age and type of a house. Types of windows include jalousie, single hung, double hung, and casement.

Chapter Quiz

1. *What type of window is located high in a wall, above eye level?*

   a. casement window
   b. clerestory window
   c. fixed window
   d. palladian window

2. *Fenestration is defined as*

   a. the arrangement of the doors and windows on a house.
   b. how many muntins and mullions are in a window.
   c. how much timber is on a property.
   d. the number of doors and windows in a house.

3. *A picture window is usually*

   a. double hung.
   b. fixed.
   c. jalousie.
   d. single hung.

4. *One of the main ingredients in drywall is*

   a. asbestos.
   b. concrete.
   c. gypsum.
   d. plaster.

5. *Which could be an ingredient in plaster?*

   a. clay
   b. glue
   c. horsehair
   d. lath

6. *Which statement about drywall is TRUE?*

   a. Drywall on ceilings is usually "abuse resistant" drywall.
   b. Drywall on ceilings is usually 1/2" because of the span of the ceiling and it is less likely to sag.
   c. Drywall on ceilings is usually 1/2" foil backed for insulation purposes.
   d. Drywall on ceilings is usually 5/8" because of the span of the ceiling and the weight of the insulation.

7. *Which type of drywall would typically NOT be used in the construction of a single-family home?*

   a. abuse resistant drywall
   b. fireproof drywall
   c. moisture resistant drywall
   d. soundproof drywall

8. *Knotty pine paneling is most closely associated with*

   a. Colonial homes.
   b. mid-century homes.
   c. new homes today.
   d. Victorian homes.

9. *Which building material would NOT contain asbestos?*

   a. asphalt floor tiles
   b. ceiling tiles
   c. plaster
   d. popcorn ceilings

10. *A swirled ceiling (one where a pattern has been placed into the ceiling with a thin coat of plaster) might indicate*

    a. asbestos is contained in the plaster.
    b. a high degree of quality in the house.
    c. a previously leaking roof.
    d. radiant electric heat.

11. *Which of these types of floor coverings is the one most recently invented and used in housing?*

    a. hardwood
    b. laminate
    c. linoleum
    d. vinyl

12. *A house with hollow core doors and metal bi-fold closet doors with louvers would most likely have been built circa the*

    a. 1890s.
    b. 1920s.
    c. 1970s.
    d. 2000s.

13. ***A fog in a sliding glass door or thermal window is an indication that***

   a. the glass was not properly cleaned before the two panes were put together.

   b. the seal is broken.

   c. there is a differential of over 40° F between the outside temperature and the inside temperature.

   d. they were not installed properly.

Chapter 5:
Plumbing

Introduction

In this chapter, we'll talk about residential plumbing systems. We will discuss how plumbing enters and exits a house, as well as the materials and fixtures that are used. We will also examine how consumer wants and needs have affected the plumbing industry.

Objectives

After completing this chapter, students will be able to:

- Describe the functions of a residential plumbing system.
- Identify types of plumbing pipe materials.
- Recall common contaminates in water and purifying methods.
- Explain how plumbing fixtures have changed over time.
- Describe how a residential septic system operates.

ABS (Acrylonitrile Butadiene Styrene) A type of plastic pipe and fittings used in plumbing; more rigid than PVC, but will deform if exposed to sunlight.

Backflow Preventer A check valve installed on the public water supply to prevent any contaminated water from a house from entering the public water main.

Blackwater Wastewater from toilets.

Brass A yellow metal made by combining copper and zinc; used for water supply lines and fittings.

Cast Iron A hard metal made from alloy, carbon, and silicon that is cast into shape; widely used in plumbing supply lines and waste lines.

Cesspool An underground container for storage of household wastewater; in the form of a concrete or metal tank, or a tank lined with logs, railroad ties, or concrete blocks.

Copper A reddish-brown colored metal; used in electrical wiring and plumbing pipes.

CPVC (Chlorinated Polyvinyl Chloride) A type of pipe used in plumbing for cold and hot water; can withstand high temperatures making it suitable for hot water lines.

Drain-Waste-Vent (DWV) System A system that removes greywater and blackwater from a building and vents air from the wastewater pipes out of the house.

Galvanized Steel A metal used for both supply and waste lines.

Greywater Household water that comes from sinks, bathtubs, dishwashers, and washing machines; it does not contain human waste.

Key Terms

(continued on page 55)

History of Plumbing

Plumbing has been around since ancient times. Ancient Romans used lead pipes for supply lines and terra cotta (clay) lines for waste lines. Evidence of plumbing was found in Ancient Greece and Asia.

PLUMBING EVENTS FROM THE 17TH THROUGH 19TH CENTURIES		
Year	Location	Event
1652	Boston	The first public waterworks was built to aid the fire brigades. The pipes at the time were wood.
1775	London	The flush toilet was patented, by a Scottish watchmaker, Alexander Cummings, who was living in London at the time. Many people think Thomas Crapper, also British, invented the flush toilet, but he actually just improved upon it.
1804	Philadelphia	The first city to use all cast iron pipes.
1829	Boston	Tremont Hotel was built with indoor plumbing. It was the first hotel in the United States to offer this amenity.
1855	Chicago	Built the first comprehensive public sewer system.
1889	Pittsburgh	Edwin Ruud, a Norwegian mechanical engineer who invented the automatic storage water heater, immigrated to Pittsburgh where he pioneered the early development of both residential and commercial water heaters.

In the United States, indoor plumbing in residential homes took quite a bit longer:

"In 1940, nearly half of houses lacked hot piped water, a bathtub or shower, or a flush toilet. Over a third of houses didn't have a flush toilet. As late as 1960, over 25% of the houses in 16 states didn't have complete plumbing facilities."

Source: James D. Lutz, Lawrence Berkley National Laboratory; Lest We Forget, A Short Housing History in the United States.

It is interesting to note how consumer expectations have changed over time with respect to residential plumbing and bathrooms. New post-WWII construction, even for four-bedroom homes, commonly had only one bathroom. Yet today, a builder would not consider building a two-bedroom condominium without at least two bathrooms.

Plumbing Functions

Plumbing is designed to provide fresh, **potable** water, and remove **greywater** and sewage. Later, we'll discuss the source of the water supply and where the sewage goes; for now, we'll discuss how plumbing works.

Water pressure is needed to ensure the plumbing coming into the house is working properly and is most often regulated by the **water pressure regulator**. Signs of low water pressure include a shower that only trickles, or filling a pot with water taking several minutes. In homes with public water systems, the first thing to check is the setting on the water pressure regulator. If there is no pressure regulator, check to see if other people on the street have low water pressure. If the neighbors have good water pressure, then the problem may be a leak or pipes with built up mineral deposits inside them.

A **main shut-off valve** should be installed at the location where the water comes into the house. This is essential, in the event of a plumbing emergency, to turn off all the water in the house until the problem can be solved.

From the main shut-off valve, the water is distributed via **pipes** to the water heater, sinks, bathtubs, washer hookups, and toilets; in short, all the plumbing fixtures.

Wastewater is removed from a house as **greywater** (everything except toilet or bidet water) or **blackwater** (comes from toilets and bidets). Local building codes vary considerably with respect to disposal of greywater. For example:

- In rural properties, cabins, or camps, where the greywater is not going into the septic or cesspool, it may be going into a dry well (which is essentially a hole filled with gravel, or possibly a container filled with gravel). In some places, the use of dry wells is 'grandfathered', meaning existing ones are allowed to remain, but new ones cannot be installed.

- In some 'green' construction, the water from showers and sinks is recycled and used to flush the toilets, before finally going into the sewer or septic system.

Plumbing fixtures require **vent pipes**, which *equalize air pressure and keep sewer gases from entering the house.*

Plumbing Materials

A variety of plumbing materials have been used over the years and like so many other things found in houses, is often installed using a mixture of materials. This is especially true with older homes, where repairs and additions have been made over time. It is not unusual to see an older home with copper, lead, galvanized steel, and PVC pipes—all in the same house!

When do-it yourselfers get involved, the results often leave home inspectors shaking their heads. For example, one remodeling job revealed that instead of using an appropriate pipe for a drain, a former owner used flexible dryer vent hose for the waste disposal under a toilet! Real estate professionals will want to identify (if possible) plumbing materials in a house and note any red flags.

Lead A soft grey metal that melts easily and was used in piping material until banned by the EPA in 1986 due to its toxicity.

Orangeburg® A waste pipe material made of lightweight wood fibers, adhesive, and coal tar, which were bound together; commonly used during the 1950s and 1960s. Also called **Fiber Conduit**.

PB (Polybutylene) A type of plastic piping used in plumbing from the 1970s through 1990; due to defective issues, it is no longer sold.

PEX Crosslinked polyethylene tubing, usually seen in blue (cold water) and red (hot water) as supply lines. Also used as tubing for radiant floor heating.

Potable Suitable for drinking.

PVC Polyvinyl chloride, used for drain lines and some supply lines.

Reverse Osmosis A process in which dissolved solids (such as salts) are removed from water. This is accomplished by household water pressure pushing the tap water through a semi-permeable membrane.

Septic System A system for disposing of sewage where there is not access to public sewer. Septic systems vary from cesspools by having drain fields.

Supply Lines The lines that supply water to the fixtures. Sinks, washing machines, bathtubs, and showers all have both hot and cold supply lines; toilets typically have only cold supply lines.

Trap A part of plumbing fixtures designed to hold water and keep sewer gas from coming up into the house. Also called "U," "S," or "J" traps.

VCP (Vitrified Clay Pipe) A pipe made from a mixture of clay that has been subjected to very high temperatures, thus "vitrifying" the pipe, which makes it a hard, inert ceramic; used in sewer pipes. The manufacturing process has been fine-tuned for centuries and was designed to be fiscally responsible, which had the added benefit of being environmentally responsible. But the primary benefit of using VCP in sanitary sewers is its long service life.

Vent Pipe A pipe (often plastic) that regulates air pressure in plumbing and keeps sewer gas from building up inside the system. Vent pipes are often stacked.

Waste Lines The lines that carry used water from the drains into the sewer or septic system.

Key Terms

Types of Plumbing Piping

Wood

The early American colonists used wood for plumbing pipes, just as they did for gutters and downspouts. Obviously, the issue with wood is rotting due to constant exposure to water. Even wood types that are resistant to rot will split under high pressure.

Cast Iron

In the early 19th century, cast iron pipes replaced wood pipes. Today, cast iron pipes are sometimes used in residential plumbing for **drain-waste-vent (DWV) systems**, which remove sewage and greywater.

Lead

By the mid-19th century, lead pipes were in wide use in the United States. Although lead was banned by the EPA in 1986, lead pipes and lead solder exist in many older homes today.

Tip

_____

To test for lead pipes, hold a magnet to an area of the pipe—a magnet will stick to cast iron and steel, but not to lead.

√ **Caution!** Before a homeowner goes about diligently removing lead pipes from the house, he should consult an electrician because lead pipes are used to ground electrical wires.

Galvanized Steel

Galvanized steel pipes came about in the late 19th century as a replacement for cast iron and lead pipes. In 1895, factories began producing seamless steel pipe. The galvanizing process involves a layer of zinc over the steel, but it corrodes over time.

Copper

The use of copper pipes began around the time of WWII, when taxes increased the cost of cast iron and steel pipes. Today, copper is expensive, yet you will see houses built with copper supply lines and waste pipes.

Orangeburg®

A post WWII product for waste lines, particularly from the house to the street, was Orangeburg® pipe. This pipe, described as "tarpaper with toilet paper mixed in" was widely installed through the 1950s and 1960s. When Orangeburg® fails, it happens quickly and completely. In one instance, a family had to replace a collapsed sewer line made of Orangeburg® pipe. It was installed in the 1950s when the house was built, and completely collapsed and was unusable by the 1970s.

PVC (Polyvinyl Chloride)

PVC was developed and used in Germany in the 1930s for sanitary drainage systems. It was first introduced into the United States in 1952 where it was used for drinking water pipes, and in the 1960s, became popular for gutters and downspouts. Today, PVC (also called vinyl) pipe is used in plumbing construction worldwide.

CPVC (Chlorinated Polyvinyl Chloride)

CPVC, a highly durable thermoplastic pipe, was developed and used in residential homes in the early 1960s. CPVC is superior to PVC in terms of its strength, ductile ability, and resistance to heated temperatures.

PB (Polybutylene)

PB was widely manufactured and used from around 1970 through 1990, although some sources claim it could still be found in building supply stores as late as 1999. PB piping failure led to a lawsuit, and a class action settlement. PB piping was advertised as being as long lasting as other building products; but in fact, it failed, often within 15 years, without warning, and with significant incidental damage to property. These pipes are blue, grey, or black. If you suspect that a house you are listing or selling has old PB pipe in it, ask a home inspector or plumber to look at it for you.

PEX (Crosslinked Polyethylene Tubing)

PEX piping was invented by a Swedish company, and first introduced in the United States in the 1980s for radiant heating. For many builders, PEX is the product of choice today as it is flexible, durable, and cheaper than other piping products.

COMPARISON OF MODERN PLUMBING PIPES			
Type	Pros	Cons	Uses
Copper	• Durable • Long service life • Corrosion resistant • Available in hard (rigid) tubes or soft tubes • Handles very high temperatures	• Expensive • Difficult to install	• Hot and cold water systems • Gas lines (soft tubes)
PVC	• Inexpensive • Installs easily • Corrosion resistant	• Brittle—can break or crack easily	• Cold water systems
CPVC	• Long service life • Corrosion resistant • Chemical resistant • Stronger and more ductile than PVC	• Manufacturing process may vary with regard to additives, lubricants, and stabilizers • More expensive than PVC	• Hot and cold water systems • Storage tanks • Fire sprinkler systems
PEX	• Long service life • Lightweight • Flexible • Installs easily • Resistant to corrosion, chemicals, heat deformation, freezing, abrasion, scratching, shrinking, stress cracks	• Some types may not provide an impermeable membrane, allowing for contamination • Can be damaged by prolonged ultraviolet light	• Hot and cold water systems • Radiant heating systems • Radiators • Hot water baseboard systems • Air conditioning systems

Plumbing Inspection

Depending upon the age and materials used for the **sewer laterals** (*the pipes from the house to the street*), in some municipalities, there is a requirement for homeowners to have them inspected and replaced if they are not functioning properly. In the past several years, technology has been developed allowing for **punch through** pipe replacement that does *not require the digging of a trench*, which was one of the most expensive aspects of replacing this line previously.

Municipal Water and Wells

Water supplied by a municipality is usually **potable** (safe to drink) because of the water tests required of municipal water companies. In many rural parts of the United States, there are community water supplies. These are often in several homes, in a village, sharing a well and/or a reservoir. Some houses have both public and private water supplies. This often happens when the house was on a private well and then public water became available. In many instances, connecting to public water is mandatory, but in many places, homeowners are allowed to keep their private well for watering gardens, washing cars, filling pools, and other uses. In these cases, the owner is required to install a **backflow preventer valve** to keep the well water from mixing with the public water.

Tip:

Note the proximity of public water to the property because FHA guidelines require connection to public water, if available, providing that the cost to connect is 3% or less of the amount of the purchase price.

Wells and springs that are not gravity fed springs will require a **pump**. Wells can be shallow or deep. A **well test** can determine how many gallons per minute the well produces. Many owners of homes with wells can tell you how deep their well is, how many gallons per minute it pumps, and how old the pump is. Occasionally, the well pump is inside the basement or crawl space of a house.

√ **Caution!** If the well itself is located within the walls of the foundation, that is a red flag for some kinds of loans, most notably FHA. The exception for FHA is properties located in arctic climates (e.g., Alaska).

Testing Water

Private well water, or spring water, should be tested periodically by the owners of the house. Buyers of homes that use wells should *always* obtain a **water test**. The tests that can be performed on private water supplies vary, and the more contaminates that are tested, the higher the price to test the water. FHA and VA have specific requirements for a water test. Beyond bacteria, they also require that the water be collected by a third party—either the testing laboratory or a home inspector.

Bacteria

The standard test for potability is to check for total **coliform bacteria**, as well as **E. coli bacteria**. The presence of either of these can make inhabitants of the home ill; although often the owner, upon receiving an unsatisfactory water test will say, "But I drink the water all the time, and I'm not sick!" One thing to consider is that people can build up a resistance to contaminated water. Infants and the elderly might get sicker sooner. Surface water can contaminate well water, as can a well being too close to an on-site sewage system, or animal waste or bodies, if the supply is a spring or reservoir.

Nitrites/Nitrates

Water is commonly tested for **nitrites** or **nitrates**. Both are forms of nitrogen. Nitrites are caused by the oxidation of nitrogen, usually from fertilizer use. Because many wells are located in rural areas, they are near farms that use fertilizer. Boiling this water only *increases* the nitrite level, making it more dangerous. Nitrates are associated with fertilizers as well as with pesticides. Both are considerably more dangerous to pregnant women and infants than to other segments of the population.

pH Test

Another test that can be performed on water supplies is a **pH test**, which reveals the level of acidity or alkalinity of water. Water with a pH less than 6.5 or more than 8.0 can cause pipe corrosion, and it will also release metals into the water including zinc, copper and lead. The solution for this problem is an acid neutralizer.

Radon

Radon can be found in well water. Radon is a naturally occurring gas; thus, the presence of radon in water is not caused by human activity. A radon test should be performed by a professional service. Often, buyers will ask sellers to test homes for radon and if detected, ask for remediation. If radon is found, the solution is an **aeration water treatment**, which mixes the water with air, or a **granular activated carbon (GAC)** system, which filters the water.

Iron and Sulphur

Some private water supplies have a high concentration of **iron**, which will stain the fixtures a reddish pink color. Symptoms of high iron content in water include dry, itchy skin; hair that is dull, not shiny, when washed; water that won't lather up well; and lime scale building up on plumbing fixtures. Another issue with some private water is a high **sulphur** content, caused by either sulfate or hydrogen sulfide in water. The tell-tale sign of sulphur is a distinctive 'rotten egg' odor. Both iron and sulphur are associated with "**hard water**," although often safe to drink, and therefore potable, is unpleasant to live with. Well **water filter systems** and **water softeners** can treat these problems.

Purifying Water

If the water is not potable, two methods are common to fix this. Both of these are designed to remove bacteria and other particles from the water and both require replacement of parts (filters, bulbs, etc.) at certain intervals, depending on the type of system.

- **Reverse osmosis systems** force water through a semi-permeable membrane, which filters out 90 to 99% of contaminants. This is used extensively in bottled water plants. The disadvantage can be a very slow flow rate.

- **Ultraviolet light** removes the germs in water by exposing them to the UV lamp, and doesn't interfere with flow.

√ **Note:** FHA, as of the time of this writing, will NOT allow a UV light to be installed to cure a bacteria problem. However, in some counties, UV light water purification is a requirement by the Department of Health. As a real estate professional, you should always be up-to-date on local, state, and federal regulations that affect property.

Plumbing for Appliances

Water Heaters

Water heaters can be electric, natural gas, propane gas, or fuel oil. Water can also be heated by a coil within a hot water or steam heating system. Some homes are set up to heat the water through the furnace and also have a stand-alone water heater, which is used during the summer months so that the furnace or boiler does not have to run to heat the water.

In recent years, on-demand, or **tankless water heaters** have grown in popularity:

- They are typically electric or gas.

- They cost more than a conventional water heater, but will pay for themselves over time.

- Unlike regular water heaters, the water is heated only when needed.

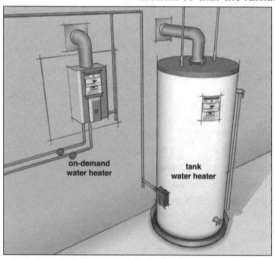

Figure 5.1: On-demand and Conventional Water Heaters
Source: U.S. Department of Energy

A formula available from the U.S. Department of Energy shows consumers how to estimate how much less (or more) each type of system takes to operate. One of the pieces of information that is necessary is what the consumer is now paying for energy; in other words, if the consumer is replacing a tank water heater with an on-demand water heater, part of the equation is what he is paying per kilowatt hour, or per cubic foot of gas.

Some homes have a **tempering tank**, which is *a large tank where water goes to be "tempered" (brought to the temperature of the basement) before being heated.* This has been observed in areas where the water coming in, especially during winter, is very cold. This can be a special tempering tank, or simply an old tank water heater, without the elements.

Most water heaters have a life span of 10 to 15 years, and are located in a variety of spaces:

- In homes with basements, water heaters are typically in the basement.

- In manufactured houses, water heaters are often hidden between two closets.

- In some parts of the country, water heaters are found in garages.

- In earthquake prone areas, building code requires that gas water heaters are strapped in place to avoid a gas leak and explosion in the event of an earthquake.

Figure 5.2: Gas Water Heating Missing Vent Pipe
Photo Courtesy of Melanie J. McLane

√ **Caution!** Gas water heaters must be vented to the outside. This photo shows a gas water heater missing the vent. This would cause gas fumes to fill the basement and is a dangerous situation!

One of the common repairs with respect to water heaters, especially for FHA and VA financing, is the installation of a pipe from the **pressure relief valve**, (sometimes called the "pop-off valve"), which is typically located at or near the top of the water heater. The pipe must extend down the side of the water heater to 6" to 12" off the floor, so that if the pressure relief valve releases hot water, it will be directed to the floor and not at someone's face.

Dishwashers

A major appliance in the kitchen that requires plumbing is the dishwasher. It requires both hot and cold water supplies, as well as a drain.

Hot water cleans dishes better than cold; the recommended temperature for dishwashers is 140° F. Yet, some experts recommend setting the temperature on the hot water heater at no more than 120° F for both safety and money savings. This problem may be solved by a dishwasher that preheats the water.

Ice Makers

Refrigerators with ice makers require a cold water line, which is usually a fairly small diameter, to supply water to make ice.

√ **Caution!** Both leaking ice maker lines and leaking dishwashers can cause significant damage, if not found promptly.

Washing Machines

In the laundry room, the washing machine requires hot and cold water, as well as a drain. Many people wash mostly in cold water; however, if any family members have dust mite allergies, hot water is recommended to get rid of dust mites in bedding.

Plumbing Fixtures

As houses have become more elaborate, builders have added more plumbing fixtures.

- Many upscale kitchens have more than one sink, a garbage disposal, a dishwasher, and possibly a special pot filler faucet near the stove.

- The standard bathroom contains three fixtures: A toilet, tub (possibly with a shower over it), and a lavatory sink. As expectations rose for bathrooms to be more upscale, builders began adding more than one sink, separate shower stalls, as well as soaker or Jacuzzi tubs, and possibly bidets.

You can often date the age of the house or the remodeling job by the color of the fixtures and ceramic tile. Additionally, the pattern of ceramic tiles can date a house.

In houses with conventional plumbing, there should be **shut-off valves** for all the plumbing fixtures. You'll find them behind the toilet, under the sink, and in the case of bathtubs and showers, usually behind a panel that is screwed into the wall. As shown in these photos, you should have a panel for access, but if one isn't there, a hole will have to be cut into the drywall to allow access to fix the pipes.

Figure 5.3: Access Panel to Plumbing (left), Hole Cut for Plumbing Access (right)
Photos Courtesy of Melanie J. McLane

As real estate professionals go through a house, they should make note of the types of plumbing materials they see and their apparent condition. Repairs are often very evident, as in this photo, showing different types of materials. The PVC piece is called a "saddle" by some plumbers, as it saddles the problem in the old pipe.

Figure 5.4: Plumbing Repair Materials; Photos Courtesy of Melanie J. McLane

Bathtubs

Original bathtubs were portable and o   **etal**. When running water
began to appear, many bathtubs were n   m had devices installed to
heat the water in the tub, because runni   example, in the Biltmore
Mansion in Asheville NC, only cold rur   he lavatory sinks; hot water
was delivered by servants for washing a

- By the 1850s, **vitreous china** wa   commodes. This material
  resisted rust and provided a smoo

- In 1880, David Buick (the same man from the Buick Automobile Company) developed
  the process of putting **porcelain enamel over a cast iron** base for sinks and tubs.

- From about 1905 on, cast iron tubs became more and more common.

- By the end of the 1920s, the Crane Company had developed a way to create colored
  porcelain fixtures.

- **Fiberglass** tubs were introduced in 1975.

- **Acrylic** bonded with fiberglass came out in the early 1980s.

- Some inexpensive housing, such as manufactured homes, features **plastic** tubs.

- At the upper end, tubs can be carved out of **marble** or a similar material.

When fiberglass was introduced, it came out with the one piece tub/shower combination for
new construction, or the three-piece fiberglass enclosure to go over the tub. At the time, this
was marketed as better than ceramic tile because it was a solid surface, with no way for water to
get behind it, as can happen with ceramic tiled areas.

Times change and everything old is new again—there is a resurgence of **ceramic tile** being
used in bathrooms. The other trend noted is that the once ubiquitous soaker tub in the master
bathroom is being replaced by the oversized shower stall, with ceramic tile, usually a seat, and
several shower heads. The large soaker, Jacuzzi tubs are not as popular, but deeper soaking tubs
are finding favor with homeowners.

Bathroom Sinks

Bathroom sinks, sometimes referred to a "lavatory sinks" were introduced with indoor plumbing, although many homes only had washbowls and pitchers well into the 20th century.

- Early sinks of **porcelain over cast iron** were pedestal sinks, which have enjoyed a resurgence of popularity.

- Mid-century houses often had colored porcelain sinks on stainless steel legs.

- The next innovation was the **vanity**, which either included a one-piece vanity top with a sink formed into the countertop, or a vanity top made of water resistant material (such as **Formica**®) into which a sink was dropped. Vanities tops made of a solid surfaces, such as Corian®, have become popular. **Corian**® was created by DuPont scientists in 1967. Since the patent expired, many other companies have since created solid surface products.

- In upscale homes, **marble**, **quartz**, and **granite** vanity tops can be found .

- Sinks of today include **ornate porcelain** with molded or painted patterns, solid **glass** bowls, **metal** bowls, etc.

Toilets and Bidets

Despite the changes in materials for tubs, toilets and bidets are still almost all made of **porcelain**. Porcelain continues to be used because it is sturdy, waterproof, and easy to keep clean and sanitary.

- Most of the innovations in toilets have to do with how much water they require to flush. **Dual flush toilets** are appearing in more and more houses. These toilets allow the user to select a 'light' or 'heavy' flush.

- **Bidets**, common in European countries, are now found in upscale bathrooms. And, when bidets show up on home improvement companies' websites, we can say that they are gaining in popularity and acceptance in the United States.

Figure 5.5: Toilet and Bidet; Photos Courtesy of Melanie J. McLane

Kitchen Sinks

Plumbing has come a long way from the enamel, single basin, wall hung sink found in your great-grandmother's house. Today's kitchen sinks can be found in various materials, colors, sizes, and configurations. Sink materials include:

- Stainless steel
- Composite granite
- Fireclay
- Cast iron
- Natural stone
- Quartz
- Solid surface
- Copper

Some sinks will have a small, higher area designed for a garbage disposal; other sinks will simply have the disposal in one side or the other of the sink. Many experts suggest either adding enzymes, or buying a specific garbage disposal, if you the house is on a septic system. The reason for this is that things that go down drains, including grease, can clog the drain field on a septic system.

Utility Sinks

A well-appointed laundry room contains a utility sink (single, double, or even triple). They are large and deep, and wonderful for cleaning very dirty things, such as sneakers, paint rollers, golf clubs, and anything else you don't want in your kitchen sink.

- Old utility sinks were made of **soapstone**, as were kitchen sinks; today, you find soapstone reappearing as a building material, especially for restoration work.

- Most inexpensive, modern utility sinks are **plastic**.

- Elaborate utility sinks are also available. For example, Kohler makes a **cast iron** utility sink with an enamel finish, and it retails for about $2,700.

Problems with Plumbing Fixtures

Clogs and leaks are the biggest problems with plumbing fixtures. Leaks can occur in the following ways:

- Inside most faucets are **washers**, which are the round, rubber circles that seal the joint in the faucet. When these dry out and the washers crack, there are small leaks in many places.

- **Compression joints**, which are found in traps and other places, have a brass or plastic ring that is compressed when the joint is tightened. Plumbers use Teflon tape on these joints to minimize leaking.

- Some leaks can go undetected for a long time. An example is the leak at the base of a toilet. Toilets sit on a flange with a **wax seal**. Sometimes, when the seal begins to leak, water will seep under the floor covering and not be detected by the homeowner until it is too late and the floor has rotted around the toilet from the constant water infiltration.

- Copper supply lines are susceptible to **pinhole leaks.** These often show up when a house has been winterized (especially if the person doing the winterization didn't do it properly).

Clogs can be caused by grease or oil, overstuffing garbage disposals, roots from trees, hair, too much toilet paper, or simply items that should not go down drains. Most public sewer lines are laid to allow gravity to do the job of transporting the waste from the laterals, to the mains, to the sewage treatment plant; however, in some places, lifts and pumps have to be installed to move the waste uphill.

Drains and Sewers

What comes into the house through the pipes will end up going out of the house through the drains. **Greywater lines** (those that carry only water from bathtubs, sinks, and washing machines) can be discarded any way possible, as long as it is downhill. Sanitary sewer lines (septic) cannot be too steep; otherwise, the liquid goes too fast and doesn't properly carry the solids out.

Most of the time, access to public sewage systems is a welcome item on a listing. The homeowner's exposure for repairs and problems, in most municipalities, is limited to interior waste lines and the **lateral line,** which is the line that goes from the house to the street; the municipality is responsible after that. There should be a **clean out** on the public sewer line. This is a capped line that allows access to clean out clogs in the sewer line. Clean outs are important access points for where the line turns; some lines turn as much as 90 degrees.

Onsite Systems

The phrase "onsite system" is one real estate professionals should add to their vocabulary whenever they are describing a property with a private sewage system and do not have *thorough documentation* of what the system is.

√ **Caution!** In rural areas, real estate professionals have found all kinds of systems used for sewage disposal, including buried 50-gallon drums. It's an area of risk, because you don't always know what is under the ground!

Cesspools

Cesspools were found in archeological excavations in Scotland, dating from 3200 BC. Their use continued for centuries, until the connection was finally made between raw sewage and disease. Early American cities had 'sewer' pipes that simply led to the nearest river or bay. As time went on, cesspools were refined by being made of tanks, either concrete or metal, or having the pit lined with logs, railroad ties, or other materials.

Cesspools are still in use in many areas and are commonly seen in use at seasonal cabin and camp properties. For recreational properties, the usage is so sporadic that they often do not create problems.

Cesspools are distinctive in that they do *not* have drain fields. A cesspool without a drain field subjected to everyday use works like a holding tank and, therefore, needs to be pumped often.

Septic System

A septic system consists of a **tank** (or tanks) and a **drain field**. The sewage goes from the house to the tank, with an inspection port, or inlet opening in that area, and another inlet opening in the distribution box area, which is where the effluent material goes from the tank to the drain field.

What goes into the tank divides into three layers:

1. The top layer is scum, which floats on the surface.
2. The middle layer is the effluent, which goes into the drain field.
3. The bottom layer is sludge, which contains the solids.

Drain fields are made of perforated pipe laid in trenches lined with gravel. These pipes can run from 60' to 140' from the tank. The perforated pipes help the liquids return to the environment in two ways:

- **Evaporation.** Evaporated water eventually returns as rain or snow.
- **Percolation.** Percolating through the soil cleans the liquids and returns them to the ground water.

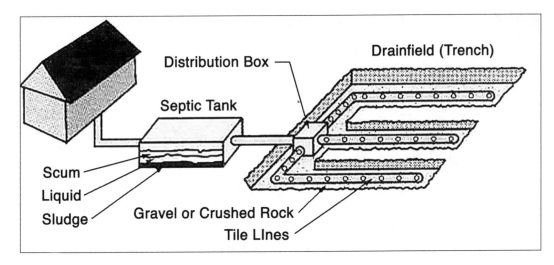

Figure 5.6: Septic System
Illustration courtesy of the United States Environmental Protection Agency

Standard septic tank sizes are usually 1,000 to 2,000 gallons and sized based on how many bedrooms are in the house, as this should be an indication of the number of occupants.

Septic systems are not maintenance free, despite the fact that many a real estate agent has been told at a listing appointment "Yes, we've lived here 20 years and never had to pump the septic!" Tanks *must* be pumped, and many municipalities now require pumping as part of their code.

Homeowners need to be cautious about what goes into a septic system: Grease and oil, coffee grounds, wipes, sanitary products, and diapers will clog a system. Also, because bacteria are beneficial for breaking down solids, homeowners need to watch how much disinfectant and bleach they use, as well as what kinds of detergents, both for dishes and clothes.

Mound (or Sand-Mound) Systems

In areas where the soil that is present will not support a conventional septic system, mound systems are installed. The mound is made of gravel and sand, and is essentially an above ground drain field. Because the mound is above grade, a pump and alarm system are required. The alarm lets the residents know that either the pump has failed or the power has gone out, and until remedied, they should not use the system.

Community Septic Systems

Some small subdivisions have a community septic, or small sewage system, which is maintained by either the developer or a homeowner's association.

√ **Note:** If this is the case, find out the age, what the cost is to maintain it, and if there is a reserve fund for major repairs.

Water and Plumbing Questions to Ask

Below is a list of suggested questions that agents need to ask property owners who are listing or selling their homes. Some of these questions may already be on the seller's property disclosure, but if they are not, it is a good practice to have these answers.

Water

1. What is the source of your water?

2. If it is public, how is the water pressure?

3. If it is a private supply, what is it—well, spring?

4. Is it shared? If so, do you have a written use and maintenance agreement with the neighbor who shares it? (Note that most title companies will require this.)

5. When was the water last tested? What were the results?

6. Do you have anything you use to filter or disinfect your water? If so, where is it, when was it installed, and how is it maintained?

7. Do you have hard water?

8. Do you have a water softener? If so, how old is it? What does it require for maintenance?

Materials and Appliances

1. What plumbing materials are in your house? When were they installed?

2. Have there been any plumbing repairs during your ownership? If so, where and why?

3. What is the source of your hot water?

4. If there is a separate water heater, how is it fueled?

5. How old is the water heater?

Sewer and Septic

1. Does the house have a private, community, or public system?

2. If it is private, is it a cesspool, a septic system, or a mound system?

3. When was it last pumped?

4. Where are the cleanout and portholes for the system are located?

5. If the house has a private water supply, what is the distance from the well to the septic?

6. Have there been any problems with the sewer lines or on-site system?

Chapter Summary

1. The purpose of plumbing in a house is to bring in potable water and remove wastewater (greywater and blackwater).

2. Water pressure is necessary for plumbing appliances and fixtures to work properly.

3. Over time, consumer expectations for indoor plumbing have changed and continue to evolve.

4. Plumbing pipes can be found in a mixture of materials: Wood, cast iron, lead, galvanized steel, copper, Orangeburg®, and various types of plastic.

5. Some municipalities require plumbing inspections of houses.

6. Water heaters can be electric, natural gas, propane gas, or fuel oil; or heated by a coil within a hot water or steam heating system.

7. Some homeowners have installed tankless (on demand) water heaters or tempering tanks that bring water to room temperature.

8. For safety, water heaters must have a working pressure relief (pop-off) value with a pipe leading to the floor for hot water to escape.

9. Public water systems and private wells are used by homeowners. Typically in rural areas, homeowners are required to 'tap in' to the public water system, if available. Many are permitted to continue to use their well water for uses other than drinking water.

10. Wells use a pump to retrieve the water. A well test can determine the number of gallons of water that are pumped.

11. Wells within the walls of the foundation may cause a buyer to not be able to secure FHA financing for a home loan.

12. Private wells and spring water should be tested periodically for contaminates, such as coliform bacteria, E. coli bacteria, nitrites or nitrates, pH, radon, iron, and sulphur. Buyers should always ask for a water test in homes with a private water source.

13. Water can be purified through a reverse osmosis system or an ultralight (UV) light water purification system. Radon can be removed using an aeration water treatment or granular activated carbon (GAC) system.

14. Plumbing styles and fixtures go in and out of style, such as ceramic tiled walls, soaker tubs, bidets, and pedestal sinks.

15. Onsite wastewater systems include cesspools and septic systems. Cesspools have been around for centuries and can be constructed using various methods. Septic system tanks divide waste into three layers: The top layer is scum that floats on the surface, the middle layer is effluent that goes into the drain field, and the bottom layer that sludge, which contains the solids.

Chapter Quiz

1. *Which of the following may be found in well water but is NOT a health hazard?*

   a. coliform
   b. E-coli
   c. nitrites
   d. sulphur

2. *Which system filters water for minerals and removes some contaminants?*

   a. aerator
   b. reverse osmosis
   c. UV light
   d. water softener

3. *Which material used during the 1950s and 1960s for lateral sewer pipes has a high record of failure?*

   a. cast iron
   b. galvanized steel
   c. Orangeburg®
   d. PVC

4. *Which pipe is often grey or black, and has a high record of failure?*

   a. CPVC
   b. PB
   c. PEX
   d. PVC

5. *Which type of piping is the product of choice today for many builders?*

   a. cast iron
   b. copper
   c. galvanized steel
   d. PEX

6. *A water heater that only heats water when needed is also known as a(n)*

   a. electric water heater.
   b. gas water heater.
   c. oil-fired water heater.
   d. tankless water heater.

7. *The pipe that goes from a house to the street where the a public sewer system is located is called the*

   a. clean out.
   b. compression joint.
   c. lateral line.
   d. U-trap.

8. *What is the solution for when soil does not allow for good drainage for a drain field?*

   a. cesspool
   b. frequent pumping
   c. mound system
   d. water tank

9. *Septic systems, through drain fields, return water to the environment by*

   a. evaporation only.
   b. percolation only.
   c. evaporation and percolation.
   d. neither evaporation or percolation.

10. *Which of the following materials was designed to withstand higher water temperatures?*

   a. ABS
   b. CPVC
   c. PE
   d. PVC

Chapter 6:
HVAC

Introduction

In this chapter, we are going to discuss heating and air conditioning systems in residential properties. The purpose of HVAC (heating, ventilation, and air conditioning) is to provide comfortable temperatures throughout the house, as well as adequate ventilation and good indoor air quality.

Objectives

After completing this chapter, students will be able to:

- Identify types of residential heating systems.
- Identify types of air conditioning systems.
- List the importance of proper ventilation in houses.

Baseboard Heat A heating system covered with a panel that is affixed horizontally along the baseboard of a wall. Can be a hot water or electric system.

Bleeding A method to remove excess trapped air in a hot water heating system.

Boiler An enclosed vessel in which water is heated and circulated, either as hot water or as steam, for heating or power.

Circulating Motor A motor used to circulate hot water or steam through the system of a house; it can also allow for different heating zones.

Conduction The transfer of heat from one area to another by the use of solids.

Convection The transfer of heat from one area to another by the use of liquids.

Creosote The by-product of burning wood, which includes smoke, water vapor, gases, unburned wood particles, hydrocarbon, tar fog, and assorted minerals. As these substances move up the chimney flue, which is colder than the stove, condensation occurs and produces a residue of these items.

Duct Tubes, canals, pipes, and vents used in a heating system to carry warm air to the house, and cold air back to the furnace.

Expansion Tank A small tank used to protect hot water heating systems from excessive pressure. The tank allows steam or hot water to expand and prevents rupturing of the pipes and fittings.

Flue A duct, pipe, or opening in a chimney that allows the smoke and waste gases to escape.

(continued on page 73)

Key Terms

Steam and Hot Water Systems

Throughout history, inventions of steam and hot water heating systems have emerged. Although too numerous to mention in this text, we will touch upon some here.

- Hot water heat was first recorded in use by a monastery, at the end of the 14th century. The monastery was in Greenland and used water from hot springs for heat.

- By the late 1700s, the French were using gravity-fed hot water systems, which later were introduced in England around 1816.

- Soon afterwards, in the U.S., Connecticut stove maker Stephen Gold experimented with steam for use in heating buildings, and in 1854, he received a patent for "Improvement in warming houses by steam." Gold invented a radiator consisting of two dimpled iron sheets that were riveted together, with rolled edges. Due to its appearance, it was coined the "mattress radiator" and was manufactured for around 50 years.

- After the Civil War, many steam heating manufacturers were built and these systems came into wide use.

How Steam and Water Systems Function

Steam and hot water systems use a **boiler**, which is *an enclosed vessel in which water is heated and circulated, either as hot water or as steam, for heating or power*. Boilers can be fueled with wood, coal, oil, natural gas, propane, or electricity for operating the following types of heating systems:

- Radiator
- Radiant floor or radiant ceiling
- Hydronic baseboard

To control the pressure in these systems, they *must* have a **pressure relief valve**, which makes certain that the pressure in the boiler does not exceed safe levels. Modern systems use one or more **pumps** to circulate the water. Gravity systems, which can still be found in older homes, have no pumps as they rely on gravity to operate.

One of the benefits of hot water and steam heat is that it is easily **zoned**, which *allows the temperature in various parts of the house to be set at different levels*, depending upon how often the room is used and what it is used for. If the thermostat is turned up, or if the temperature drops, the system kicks on and begins circulating the water throughout the house.

Here is a photo of circulating motors on an **oil-fired hot water system**, which has four zones for various parts of the house. Note the **expansion tank** at the top, left-hand side of the photo. This tank *controls the pressure in the water heating system*.

Figure 6.1: Oil Fired Hot Water System, Photo Courtesy of Melanie J. McLane

Maintenance of Steam and Hot Water Systems

Water must be added to steam systems periodically; these boilers have a **low water cut-off valve**, so the system will simply shut off if there is not enough water to run it. The valve is usually clear glass, which allows the homeowner to monitor the water level, and if low, add water to the system.

A cool radiator in a house where the other radiators are warm could indicate a problem, depending on whether the radiator is steam or hot water:

- **Steam radiator** – The pressure relief valve may be clogged with minerals or stuck shut. It may be possible to unclog the valve, but replacement is recommended.

- **Hot water radiator** – The radiator needs to be bled. **Bleeding** the radiator *gets rid of trapped air in the system*. This is much less complicated than it sounds. A screwdriver or a small tool known as a "key" is used to turn the valve until the excess air comes out. Afterwards, water may need to be added to the system.

Another issue causing a radiator to not heat could be the settling of the house. The pipe connected to the radiator no longer slopes downward to the boiler, and water is pooling in the pipe. To remedy this, the radiator could be raised up or, for a more major fix, the plumbing could be redirected.

Annual maintenance of boilers should be done by a qualified service professional, who will inspect the burner and check the controls and gauges.

Steam v. Hot Water Radiators

Radiators can be steam systems or hot water systems.

- The **hot water radiator** is a two-pipe system: One with hot water coming in and the other with cold water going out.

- The **steam radiator** is a one-pipe or two-pipe system with the steam rising and cold water falling.

In many cases, these radiators are interchangeable and can be converted from one to the other.

The basic function of the two systems is as follows:

- **Steam radiators** are upright units with air vents that open as the steam boosts the air pressure inside the radiator. When the steam hits the vents, it closes them. The radiator then 'radiates' heat into the room. As the steam inside the radiator cools, it returns to a liquid state, and through gravity, returns to the boiler where it is reheated.

- **Hot water radiators** are either the upright, like the steam radiator, or a baseboard design. Both use hot water in the pipes to produce heat. Hot water baseboard heat typically has copper pipes with fins that help radiate the heat.

Pressure Relief Valve A valve found on hot water and steam systems, as well as on water heaters, which releases steam and pressure should the temperature inside the furnace, boiler, or hot water heater get too hot.

Radiant Heat Heat energy that is transmitted by electromagnetic waves; not transmitted by conduction or convection.

Radiator A heating device consisting of a series of connected pipes, typically inside an upright metal structure, through which steam or hot water is circulated, and radiates heat into the surrounding space.

Swamp Cooler A type of air conditioning system that runs air over saturated pads.

Thermostat A device used to regulate the heat or air conditioning coming from the system.

Zoning The distribution of heat in a house to control temperature levels in various rooms. In hot water systems, zone valves control the distribution of the hot water and the output of heat.

Key Terms

Both steam and hot water systems are **closed systems**, meaning that *the water or steam circulates within the system.* If the system is on a public water supply and there is a leak, the system will continue to 'call' for water, which will result in an ongoing leak. Sadly, there have been homes where pipes have broken, and the ensuing flood coated the walls and floors with water, which turned to ice.

This photo of a radiator is from a house that was 'winterized'—by an apparently clueless contractor. All of the ends of the radiators had blown off, as there was still water in the system, and when they froze, they expanded.

Figure 6.2: Radiator with Ice; Photo Courtesy of Melanie J. McLane

Radiant Hot Water and Electric Heat

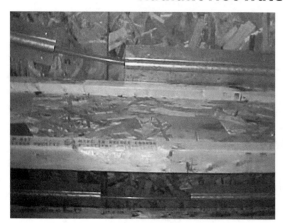

All radiant heat works on the principle that **infrared radiation** delivers the heat from the heated surface to the room. The effects of this can be observed by going outdoors on a hot day, and feeling the heat radiate from the sidewalk, pavement, and buildings.

Indoors, radiant heat is preferred by many who enjoy warms floors and comfortable room temperatures. Radiant heat has no visible ducts, vents, pipes, radiators, or baseboard heaters and can be produced with water, electric, or warm air; although water is becoming the more popular choice with the advent of PEX piping, which is durable and flexible. This photo shows a system with tubes that carry hot water.

Figure 6.3: Radiant Floor Heat; Photo Courtesy of Melanie J. McLane

Many people prefer radiant heat for a variety of reasons:

- Radiant heat is considered to be more efficient than heat supplied by ducts, because it doesn't lose heat during the delivery.
- Generally, radiant heat is more even.
- For allergy sufferers, there is no duct work to hold allergens.
- For those interested in home décor, there is no concern about not placing furniture over a duct, or in front of a run of hot water baseboard.

Radiant Ceiling Heat

Radiant heating units were also installed in ceilings—using either hot water or electricity. With older hot water ceiling systems, one drawback was the heat near the ceiling was warm while the floor remained cold. Thus, many homeowners opted to replace their radiant ceiling heating systems with a system that was more comfortable. In one such house built in the 1950s, the owners converted the ceiling heat to a heat pump, and made certain a compressor was used to remove any water from the cast iron pipes in the ceiling to avoid future leaks and damage.

With electric ceiling systems, radiant heat cable, tubing, wires, or panels are installed. In some older houses, one way to recognize it is by a distinctive swirled ceiling pattern. Most often, if there is radiant heat in the ceiling of a house, it is likely to be electric.

Hot, Warm, or Forced Air Systems

Hot air systems have been around since the ancient Romans, who primarily used them to heat public baths. They built **hypocaust systems**, which is a type of underfloor heating. Basically, *the floor was constructed of tile and concrete, which sat on a series of stacked support pillars, raising it above ground. Heat and smoke from burning wood was generated underneath the floor, which passed through tile flues inside the walls, heated the floors and walls, and escaped through the roof.*

Hot Air Gravity Furnaces

Early hot air systems were **gravity systems**, without blowers or motors. The premise of these systems is based on physics—hot air rises and cold air falls. They were designed to burn coal or wood, although coal became more widely used in the mid-19th century. These systems often had one large grate in the center of the first floor through which the heat came up from the furnace in the basement.

Coal furnaces were **hand fired**, meaning *someone had to keep the fire burning, add coal as needed, and take out the ashes.* To store the coal for these furnaces, **coal bins** were installed in the basement. The coal was delivered to the bin through a chute, usually built in a basement window. A big improvement was the **"worm fed" system**, so called because the *transmission of coal was called a "feed worm."* This device, which appeared around 1912, fed coal to the furnace in measured amounts all day and all night.

Later, gravity systems were installed with ducts and cold air returns. These large, round furnaces were sometimes called "octopuses" because they had large 'arms' (ducts) that branched out in all directions to the rooms above. Some of these furnaces were converted to oil or natural gas.

Problems with Heat Distribution

In many older homes, the distribution of heat from hot air gravity furnaces, and other heating systems, may be inadequate. There may be parts of the house that either do not have heat, or are always cold because those rooms are far away from the heat source.

√ **Note:** Some lending programs require heat in *all rooms*. Therefore, appraisers will only 'count' heated square footage, so any unheated space, such as a sunroom or enclosed porch, will not be considered in the square footage.

Forced Air Heating Systems

Forced air heating systems began after electric fans were developed. These systems use a fan or blower to 'force' the warm air from the furnace through the ducts and out the registers into the rooms. Air is returned to the furnace through large vents on the walls. A thermostat connected to the furnace controls the temperature within a house. Filters installed in the furnaces help to prevent dust and allergens from returning to the air. Types of forced air systems include natural gas, propane, electric, heat pump, or hydronic coil. Forced air is the heating system choice for most consumers in North America today.

Invention of the Electric Thermostat

Like most inventions, the electric thermostat was invented to solve a specific need. College professor Warren S. Johnson, who taught in Wisconsin, would become annoyed at the fluctuating temperatures in his classroom. The only way to adjust the heat was to find the janitor, and send him to the basement to adjust the valves on the steam system. This likely prompted Johnson to develop the electric annunciator system, which simply rang a bell to signal the janitor to adjust the heat. Johnson kept experimenting, and by 1885, he patented the electric thermostat and started Johnson Electric Service Company to manufacture his product. The company is still in business today as Johnson Controls.

Wood, Pellet, Coal Stoves, and Burners

Beginning in the 1970s, when the Arab Oil Embargo increased the cost of fuel oil and gasoline substantially, homeowners began to explore alternative heating systems for their homes. Many of them installed wood stoves, pellet stoves, coal stoves, and even wood furnaces. Some of these stoves were inserts into existing fireplaces, some were separate and in the main living areas, and some were installed in basements to provide heat through existing duct work.

One of the first things to check when a home has any of these types of heat is whether or not it is an auxiliary heating system or the main heating system.

√ **Note:** The Fannie Mae guidelines state that heat must be "permanent and automatic."

Many owners exclusively use these stoves or furnaces, but have an automatic heat source in place to satisfy lender requirements, and so they can leave the house for extended periods in cold weather and not worry about the heat burning out.

Chimney Flues

A heating system that burns oil, coal, or wood requires a **flue**, which is *a duct, pipe, or opening in a chimney that allows the smoke and waste gases to escape*. Flues can deteriorate over time, making them no longer safe to use. In this photo, you can see that bricks have fallen away from the flue. Old brick is very soft and disintegrates over time.

Figure 6.4: Deteriorated Flue
Photo Courtesy of Greg Hancock, Hancock Home Inspections

Burning of wood produces **creosote**, which can build up and catch on fire in a flue, or clog it up. If the flue is clogged, carbon monoxide will build up in the house. **Carbon monoxide (CO)** is *an odorless, colorless gas that can be fatal*. It is recommended that any house that uses gas, wood, or coal also have a **carbon monoxide detector**. Chimney flues should be cleaned and inspected at least annually for blockages or leaks.

√ **Caution!** According to residential code, it is *never* acceptable for a pellet stove or wood stove or furnace to share a flue with another furnace.

Heat Pumps

The invention of the heat pump is an example of a fortunate accident. According to several sources, in the late 1940s, Robert C. Webber, an American inventor, was experimenting with his deep freezer and accidentally burned his hand on the outlet pipe. This lead to an 'aha!' moment for Webber, who connected the outlet pipe to a hot water heater, then put the hot water through a loop. He later added a fan to move the warm air. By this time, we already had refrigeration, and the by-product of refrigeration is heat. Lord Kelvin, a Scottish scientist in the 19th century, had laid the groundwork for modern refrigeration (recall that early refrigerators were called "Kelvinators"), and as happens in science, Webber built on his ideas.

Heat pumps work on the transfer of heated air from one place to another as seen in this diagram. This is why in winter heat pumps make the house warm, and in summer, make a house cool.

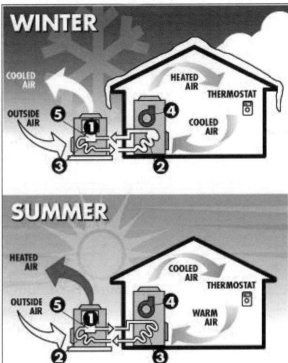

Figure 6.5: Conventional Heat Pump; Source: U.S. Department of Energy

Heat pumps have a refrigeration system that has a compressor and two coils made of copper tubing, one usually inside and one outside. There are aluminum fins that aid the transfer of the heat. The system contains a liquid refrigerant, often **Freon**, *a class of liquid or gaseous fluorocarbon or chlorofluorocarbon products, used as refrigerants.* The liquid refrigerant in the outside coils extracts heat from the air, which is then evaporated into a gas. As the coils take the gas into the house, it condenses back into a liquid, releasing the heat. A reversing valve is used for cooling.

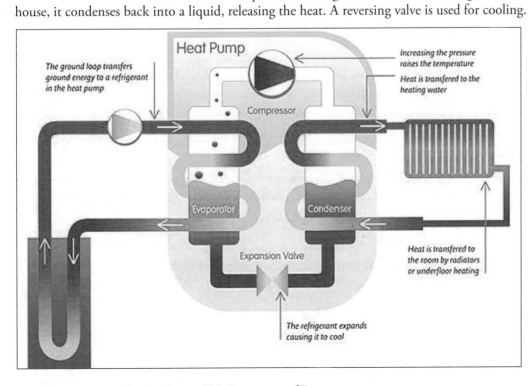

Figure 6.6: Heat Pump System; Source: U.S. Department of Energy

There are a variety of heat pumps, from older less efficient models, to newer state-of-the-art models. The Department of Energy identifies four types of heat pumps:

- Air-source
- Ductless mini-split
- Geothermal
- Absorption

Most heat pumps are **split-systems**, meaning that *one coil is inside and one is outside*. A basic heat pump is a single zone system; often, if you see two outdoor condensers, it indicates two zones.

√ **Note:** Many heat pump systems will both heat and cool the air, but some homes have separate systems for each.

Air-source Heat Pumps

Air-source heat pumps are the most common heat pumps found and usually utilize existing duct work; however, ductless systems can be installed in some areas, such as an addition to a house.

Ductless Mini-split Heat Pumps

Ductless mini-split heat pumps are appearing more often in houses, especially when it is expensive to install a regular system and the owners are seeking to cool a small house, or part of a larger house. These units are often hung on a wall towards the ceiling, and operated by remote control.

Geothermal Heat Pumps

Ground source heat pumps are sometimes referred to as **geothermal heat pumps**. Ground source heat pumps work on the principal that the temperature below the frost line is relatively the same year round. Although this temperature varies, an average is around 50 °F, which makes it more efficient than, for example, trying to heat 10°F or cool 90°F outside air.

Ground source heat pumps, in some applications, result in **zero net energy buildings**, meaning *the building produces all of the heat and air conditioning it uses.*

There are several kinds of ground source heat pumps, including ones that are closed loop, and ones that utilize an existing body of water. Some have 'slinky' type loops in the ground.

√ **Caution:** It is critical that geothermal heat pump system be right sized for the house. Those that are improperly sized may freeze up in extreme weather, leaving the homeowner without any heat.

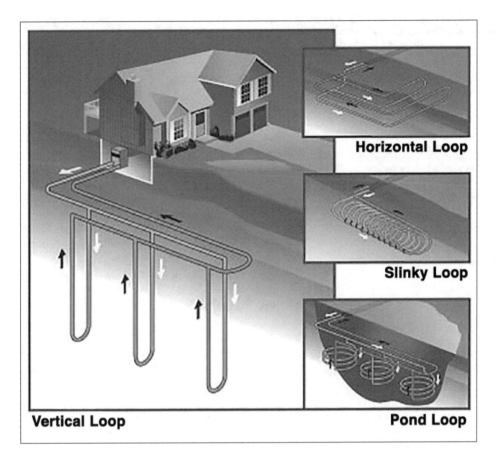

Horizontal Loop

Slinky Loop

Vertical Loop

Pond Loop

Figure 6.7: Geothermal Systems
Source: U.S. Department of Energy

Absorption Heat Pumps

Absorption heat pumps are more common in industrial or commercial uses; although they can be found in large houses. A 5-ton system is designed for use in houses of 4,000 or more square feet. They are driven by a heat source, which can be natural gas, propane, or even solar heated or geothermal heated water, but are most commonly fired by gas.

Most absorption heat pumps are used for cooling *o*nly. However, in the application where they are used for both heating and cooling, they use ammonia as a refrigerant, and operate much like a regular heat pump. The ammonia is not pumped into the compressor, but instead is absorbed into water. To remove the ammonia from the water, the heat source (gas) boils the ammonia out of the water.

COMPARISON OF COMMON HEATING SYSTEMS				
Type	**Heat Source**	**Delivery Method**	**Pros**	**Cons**
Forced Air	• Furnace or heat pump – natural gas, propane, oil, or electric	• Blower forces air through ductwork and out registers	• Efficient • Moderate installation cost • Air can be filtered • Can control humidity	• Requires ductwork • Fan can be heard • Filters must be changed regularly • Requires regular maintenance
Radiant	• Boiler or water heater or heat pump water heater – steam or hot water	• Radiant floor system, or radiant wall or ceiling panels	• Efficient • Quiet operation • Even, long-lasting heat • Comfortable heat at lower temperatures	• High installation cost • Parts are scarce • Slow heating cycle • Ceiling system may cause uneven heat distribution • Difficult access for maintenance issues
Radiator (Water or Steam)	• Boiler– steam or hot water	• Upright cast iron unit	• Efficient • Even, long-lasting heat • Reliable • Low maintenance	• Parts are scarce • Hot to the touch • Prone to banging sounds • Decorating around it could be a challenge
Baseboard (Hydronic)	• Boiler with baseboard mounted panels – water or oil	• Convection – draws in cold air and releases hot air that rises	• Efficient • Quiet operation • Ductwork is not required	• Slow heating cycle • Can produce uneven heat in different rooms • Requires regular maintenance
Baseboard (Electric)	• Baseboard mounted panels – electric	• Convection – draws in cold air and releases hot air that rises	• Quiet operation • Even heat • Easy to install • Ductwork is not required • Low maintenance	• Inefficient, costly to operate
Geothermal	• Heat pump – water or antifreeze	• Loops buried in the ground circulate heat to and from the earth	• Very efficient • Quiet operation • Low cost to operate • Long life • Environmentally friendly	• Expensive to install • Filters must be changed regularly • Requires regular maintenance

Source of Fuels for Home Heating

This chart, from the U.S. Department of Energy, shows the breakdown of fuels used for home heating across the United States.

The chart reveals that natural gas is the strong leader, followed by electricity, and then fuel oil. Together, liquid petroleum gas (also called propane) and "other" make up the least used.

There are also many systems that employ multi-fuels (e.g., wood, coal, or kerosene). Some are designed to burn liquid petroleum (LP) gas.

Figure 6.8: Fuels Used for Heating U.S. Homes

Figure 6.9: Outdoor Furnace; Photo Courtesy of Melanie J. McLane

A multi-fuel outdoor furnace is one such system. The rationale for some owners for an outdoor furnace is safe, efficient, and cost effective. This photo shows an **outdoor furnace** in a rural area.

Air Conditioning

As with heating systems, the path to air conditioning took many twists and turns.

- In 1851, the first U.S. patent for an early form of air conditioning was granted to Dr. John Gorrie for a machine that created ice by using a compressor powered by wind-driven sails, water, or horses. Despite receiving the patent, he never brought this technology to market, and the only relief from hot weather was the use of fans.

- In 1902, engineer Willis Carrier was working for the Buffalo Forge Company, and was asked to solve a problem a lithographic firm was having with magazine pages sticking together because of humidity. Willis came up with and got a patent for "*Apparatus for Treating Air*," which could both remove or add humidity. His system used cooling coils, and he also devised a control system to control both heat and humidity. Carrier, along with six other engineers, left Buffalo Forge to form Carrier Engineering Corporation.

- By 1904, at the St. Louis World's Fair, the Missouri State Building was cooled by mechanical refrigeration.

- By the 1920s, movie theatres were air conditioned, which brought crowds in on hot afternoons. Most of these systems were modified heating systems, which lead to very uneven temperatures throughout the theatre.

- By the early 1930s, General Electric was producing home air conditioning units, which were bulky and expensive. H. H. Schultz and J. Q. Sherman got a patent for a window air conditioner; these went on sale in 1932, but few were sold because they were still quite expensive. The cost at the time was between $10,000 and $50,000, which equates to $120,000 to $600,000 today! However, inventors kept tinkering with the product, making it smaller, cheaper, and more efficient.

- By 1947, Henry Galson had helped develop production lines for making air conditioners; the price came down, and in that year, 43,000 window air conditioners were sold.

> ## The Whole House Fan
>
> *The **whole house fan** was popular in the 1950s through the 1960s as a cheaper alternative to air conditioning. Whole house fans were installed in the attic. They were large, and often noisy, but effectively removed the hot air in the upper part of the house. Whole house fans worked well when combined with other energy saving methods. One of which is to close up the house early in the day, including blinds, draperies and curtains, as well as closing doors and windows. At dusk, the homeowner would turn on the fan, open the basement door and the windows, including those in the cellar, and pull the warm air out of the house. This could drop the temperature by at least 10 degrees.*

Air conditioning, once a 'high end' feature, is now mainstream. This graph from the U.S. Energy Information Administration, as of 2009, shows how many homes now have central air conditioning.

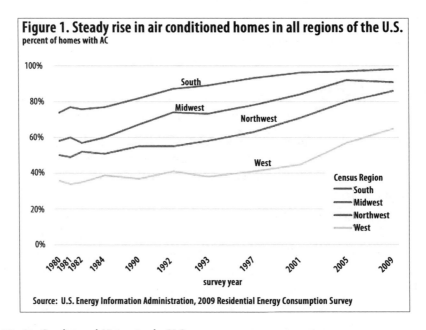

Figure 6.10: Air Conditioned Homes in the U.S.

Usage is highest in the South, with the Midwest and Northeast close behind. It is lowest in the West, due to low humidity and low overnight temperatures. In these areas, some people use **swamp coolers**. *Outdoor air is passed over water saturated pads, causing the water to evaporate, and drop the temperature by 15 to 40 degrees.* These systems are cheaper and require more maintenance, but are not suitable for areas with high humidity.

Ventilation

The 'V' in HVAC stands for 'ventilation.' Houses need ventilation to remove excess steam from cooking and showers, to remove odors, and to provide a good indoor air quality.

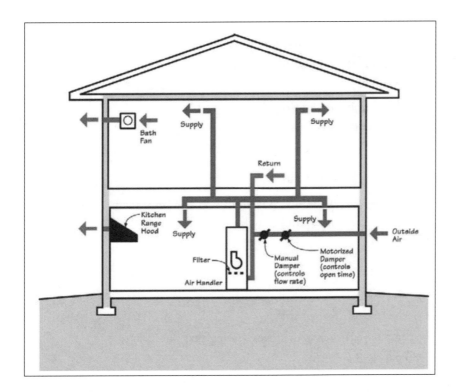

Figure 6.11: Home Ventilation; Illustration Courtesy of U.S. Department of Energy

Poor indoor air quality can make the residents sick and aggravate certain health problems, such as allergies and asthma. Indoor air quality in a poorly ventilated house can be four- to-five times worse than the outside air quality! Here's a list of major indoor air polluters:

- Radon
- Mold and mildew
- Cigarette and cigar smoke
- Volatile Organic Compounds (VOCs)

√ **Note:** VOCs are *a large group of carbon-based chemicals that easily evaporate at room temperature*. VOCs are found in building materials, home and personal care products, paint, and other items found in homes.

Bathroom and kitchen fans should remove some air polluters; however, certain hood/fan combinations over a stove just circulate the air. The preference is to vent cooking odors and smoke to the outside, although in some homes, kitchen and bathroom fans are vented into the attic. Unfortunately, this warm, moist air in the attic can contribute to mold growth, causing even more indoor air quality issues.

HVAC Questions to Ask

Below is a list of suggested HVAC questions that agents need to ask property owners who are listing or selling their homes.

Heat

1. What kind of heat does the house have?
2. Does it have more than one kind of heat?
3. Is it zoned?
4. If it is a furnace or boiler, how old is it?
5. When was it last cleaned and serviced?

Fuel

1. What fuel(s) do you use to heat?
2. What is the approximate annual consumption (gallons, cubic feet, kilowatt hours)?
3. What was the cost for the most recent year?

Flues

1. Does the system use a flue?
2. Where is the flue?
3. Has it been cleaned? If so when?
4. Are there any other furnaces or stoves sharing that flue?
5. Have you ever had a flue fire?

Ventilation

1. Have you noticed any mold or mildew in the house?
2. Are there persistent, unpleasant odors?
3. Have you had the duct work cleaned? If so, when?
4. Do the fans in the kitchen and bathrooms vent to the outside or to the attic?
5. Are there fans in all the bathrooms?

Chapter Summary

1. Steam and hot water systems use a boiler to heat the water, which runs through pipes to distribute the heat. Boilers can be fueled with wood, coal, oil, natural gas, propane, or electricity.

2. Radiator, radiant floor or ceiling, and hydronic baseboard systems require minimal maintenance—mainly, adding water or bleeding to remove trapped air, depending on the type of system.

3. Radiant floor heat that is produced with hot water is gaining in popularity due to the advent of PEX piping, which is durable and flexible.

4. Radiant ceiling heat can be produced with water or electric; though electric is used more often.

5. Early hot air systems were gravity systems without blowers or motors and were powered with wood or coal. Coal became more widely used. Later, gravity systems, called "octopuses," included ducts and cold air returns.

6. Forced air heating systems began after the electric fan was developed.

7. Wood, pellet, and coal stoves and burners became popular in the 1970s when the price of heating fuel increased substantially. Many homeowners subsidized these units with an automatic heat source.

8. A heating system that burns oil, coal, or wood requires a flue. A flue should be cleaned regularly to remove creosote, which can build up and cause a fire or clog the flue.

9. Heat pumps work on the transfer of heated air from one place to another. There are four types of heat pumps: Air-source, ductless mini-split, geothermal, and absorption.

10. The U.S. Department of Energy identified fuels used for heating U.S. homes, in this order: 1. Natural gas, 2. Electricity, 3. Fuel oil, 4. Liquid petroleum gas, and 5. Other.

11. Early air conditioning units were too expensive for most homeowners. Later, air conditioners became smaller, more efficient, and more affordable.

12. Proper ventilation in houses is vital for removing excess steam from bathrooms, removing kitchen smoke and odors, and providing good indoor air quality. Poor indoor air quality can make residents sick and aggravate certain health problems.

13. Major indoor air polluters include radon, mold and mildew, cigarette and cigar smoke, and organic compounds (VOCs).

Chapter Quiz

1. *Which type of system requires an expansion tank?*

   a. gas forced air
   b. heat pump
   c. hot water
   d. pellet stove

2. *A knocking sound in a radiator could indicate*

   a. a leak.
   b. valves are not closing properly.
   c. a very cold day, as the heat adjusts.
   d. water in the system.

3. *Which is the most common source of fuel for residential heating in the United States?*

   a. coal
   b. fuel oil
   c. natural gas
   d. propane

4. *Which type of heat is considered the most efficient?*

   a. electric
   b. geothermal
   c. natural gas
   d. wood

5. *What heating system has no visible ducts, vents, pipes, radiators, or baseboard heaters?*

   a. electric
   b. geothermal
   c. hand fired coal
   d. radiant

6. *The founder of American company_____ patented thermostats for steam heat.*

   a. Carrier Corporation
   b. IBM
   c. Johnson Controls
   d. Kelvinator

7. *Which was an innovation in coal heating?*

   a. coal bins
   b. grates to remove cinders
   c. octopus furnace
   d. worm fed system

8. *Which statement is TRUE for a house heated entirely by a wood stove?*

   a. Fannie Mae will not accept a heating system that is not automatic.
   b. Fire insurance rates will be lower.
   c. The house will be more comfortable than other homes.
   d. The woodstove must be an outdoor furnace.

9. *All heat pumps*

   a. are geo-thermal.
   b. are ground source.
   c. are highly efficient.
   d. work on the transfer of heat from one place to another.

10. *Swamp air conditioners are*

    a. best suited for areas with low humidity.
    b. best suited for high-humidity climates; hence why they are called "swamp."
    c. more expensive than regular air conditioners.
    d. the most popular kind of air conditioning in use.

11. *A house with 4,000 or more square feet might use which unit?*

    a. absorption heat pump
    b. ductless mini-split heat pump
    c. several warm air furnaces
    d. swamp air conditioner

12. *Which was a more economical alternative to central air conditioning in terms of operational cost?*

    a. absorption heat pump
    b. heat pump with two condensers
    c. several room air conditioners
    d. whole house fan

Chapter 7:
Wiring

Chapter Introduction

In this chapter, we will discuss the progression of electricity from early eras to today's modern electrical systems, and how the use of electricity for labor-saving devices has radically changed American homes. We will also examine the dangers of electricity and the safety measures that ensued.

Chapter Objectives

After completing this chapter, students will be able to:

- Identify inventions and contributions that lead to modern electrical household systems and appliances.
- Explain the basic way household electricity functions.
- Explain the importance of grounding.
- Recall the dangers in electrical wiring.

Key Terms

Alternating Current (AC) An electric current that reverses direction at regular intervals.

Ampere (Amp) The basic unit of electrical current.

Circuit Breaker An automatically operated electrical switch designed to protect an electrical circuit from damage caused by overcurrent/overload or short circuit. Its basic function is to interrupt current flow after protective relays detect a fault.

Circuit Panel A component of an electricity supply system that divides an electrical power feed into subsidiary circuits, while providing a protective fuse or circuit breaker for each circuit, in a common enclosure. Also called a **Breaker Panel or Box**.

Direct Current (DC) An electric current flowing in only one direction. Direct current can be produced by a power source, batteries, solar cells, or dynamos.

Fuse A device containing a conductor that melts when excess current runs through an electric circuit, opening and thereby protecting the circuit.

Ground Fault Circuit Interrupter (GFCI) A device installed in an electrical outlet that shuts off an electric power circuit when it detects that current is flowing along an unintended path. GFCIs are required by code to be in kitchens, baths, and other areas of the house.

Grounding A safety measure to help prevent electrical shock by use of 'grounding rods' to direct electric current into the ground in the event of a lighting strike, or other mishap.

(continued on page 89)

Electricity and Houses

It is hard to imagine a house without electricity. Homeowners use electricity to heat and cool, to cook and keep food cold, for lighting to read and do other tasks, to watch TV, or to surf the Internet. Electricity is found in virtually every house, unless the owners selected not to install it, such as in an Amish home, or because it is not near power lines, such as in a very remote cabin. Yet, many very remote cabins are still wired and run off generators. As is true for the other systems we find in houses, electricity was introduced gradually, and improvements continue to be made. The building code requirements for electricity also continue to evolve, as people use more power, and more safety features are invented.

History of Household Electricity

Electricity for household use began in the 1800s and has since evolved. Let's discuss some of the more significant advances.

- Joseph Swan, an Englishman, invented the first **light bulb** in 1878. However, his light bulb burned out very quickly.

- Also in 1878, Thomas Edison founded the **Edison Electric Light Company**, and began experimenting with a **long-lasting light bulb** that could burn for about 40 hours. By 1880, Edison's light bulbs could be used for 1,200 hours.

- In 1879, the **California Electric Light Company**, in San Francisco, began selling electricity to customers.

- In 1882, the world's first central power plant started generating direct current (DC) electricity. The plant, **Pearl Street Station**, was located on Pearl Street in New York City. It was built by the **Edison Illuminating Company**, headed by Thomas Edison. The Pearl Street Station could generate power only for properties in close proximity to the plant.

- Also in 1882, the world's first hydroelectric power plant, **Appleton Edison Light Company**, began operation in Appleton, Wisconsin on the Fox River. The man behind it was H. J. Rogers, owner of a paper company in Appleton, who had studied Edison's inventions.

- In 1891, Nikola Tesla, invented the "**Tesla coil**," which changed electricity from low voltage to high voltage. This made it easier for electricity to travel over long distances. Tesla was an alternating current (AC) proponent, which was in direct *opposition* to Edison's position to continue using direct current (DC).

- Building on Tesla's ideas, William Stanley, Jr., an American inventor and engineer, developed the first practical **transformer**. He also improved on the **electric meter**. He worked with AC, and is credited with making electric power a possibility across vast areas.

- During this highly creative period, Tesla rolled out, in 1888, the first **polyphase alternating current system**. This system made electrical production and use possible, and included generators, transformers, transmissions systems, motors and lights. George Westinghouse of the **Westinghouse Electric & Manufacturing Company** bought the patent rights to this AC system, seeing its huge potential. In 1893, Westinghouse used an AC system to light the Chicago World's Fair.

- In 1895, Charles Proteus Steinmetz received a patent for "*System of distribution of alternating current.*"

- By 1896, an **AC powerline** that transmitted power from Niagara Falls to Buffalo New York was opened; this covered a distance of 20 miles.

- By the 1930's, most Americans had electricity in their houses, except those who lived in rural areas. Farmers and ranchers across the United States used kerosene lamps for lighting and doing countless household chores by hand, such as pumping and hauling water for people and animals. To press clothing, women used solid cast irons called "sad irons" that were five to nine pounds, which were heated on wood stoves. One future President of the United States, Lyndon Johnson, observed his mother struggling with these household chores. Once elected to Congress, Johnson succeeded in bringing electricity to the "Hill Country" in Texas where his family had lived.

- Much of the efforts to electrify rural America came under programs in the **New Deal** era (1933-1938), when many rural cooperatives were created to generate and sell electricity. Cooperatives are still found in many parts of the United States.

History of Common Household Appliances

In the 1900s, inventors were looking at other ways to use electricity, particularly in household appliances.

- James Spangler, an asthmatic janitor, realized that the dust he swept aggravated his asthma. He tinkered around with a soap box, broom handle, and an old fan motor, and using a pillowcase to collect the dust, came up with an **electric vacuum cleaner** that he used in his job at a department store in Canton, Ohio. In 1908, once he improved on this model and added attachments, he received the patent. He formed his own company, and his cousin's husband, William Hoover, was so impressed with his invention that he bought into the company, which became the **Hoover Company** in 1922. Hoover became synonymous with vacuuming, to the point where it entered the language as the verb "hoovering" the floors.

- There is disagreement among sources about who first invented the electric **washing machine**, but the Thor machine, invented by Alva J. Fisher, was built and sold in 1908 by the **Hurley Machine Company** of Chicago. This was the first machine to use an electric motor and a galvanized tub, and was also less heavy and bulky than other, earlier machines.

- Credit is given to Fred W. Wolf, Jr. for invention of the electric **refrigerator**. Wolf named his invention the DOMELRE, which is an acronym for DOMestic ELectric REfrigerator.

- Although electricity was added later, the first **dishwasher** was invented by a woman, Josephine Cochrane. She unveiled her dishwasher at the 1893 World's Fair in Chicago.

Junction Box A plastic or metal container for electrical connections, usually intended to conceal them from sight and deter tampering.

Mast A rigid, hollow pole with a service cap on top of it, typically installed on the roof or the upper side of an outside wall.

New Deal A series of domestic programs enacted by the U.S. between 1933 and 1938. The programs were in response to the Great Depression and focused on relief, recovery, and return.

Nob-and-Tube Wiring A type of wiring commonly used decades ago where open electric wires are supported on knobs and encased in tubes in areas where they pass through beams or partitions.

Service Entrance The point where electricity enters a house from the power supplied and goes into the meter.

Volts A measure of electric potential. This is the energy that could be released if the electric current is allowed to flow.

Key Terms

Her invention had a wooden wheel that laid flat in a copper boiler, which could be turned by hand or driven by a power source using a pulley. Restaurant owners were very interested, and so she opened a factory, which became **KitchenAid**. For many years, dishwashers were too expensive for the middle class; it is estimated that their cost in 1960 was equal to a housekeeper's annual salary, but as the technology grew, the prices came down and market penetration began.

Impact of Electricity on Housing Equipment

The following statistics are from the *HUD 2009 American Housing Survey* on housing equipment:

- 100% of units have a refrigerator and kitchen sink.
- 99% of all homes have a cooking stove or range.
- 60% of cooking fuel is electricity.
- 35% of cooking fuel is piped gas.
- 66% of homes have a dishwasher.
- 51% have a garbage disposal.
- 84% have a washing machine.
- 81% have a clothes dryer.
- 65% have central air-conditioning (89% for new homes).
- 21% have window air-conditioning units
- 93% reported a smoke detector
- 36% reported having a working carbon monoxide detector.

Electrical Power to Houses

Unless a generator is used to create electrical power for a house, the electricity is generated off site and transmitted to the house. The electrical transmission and distribution system or 'power grid' supplies electricity from the power plants to homes.

- The power enters the house by underground or overhead wiring.
- If the wiring comes in from a pole above grade, it enters a **mast**, which is *a rigid, hollow pole with a service cap on top of it, typically installed on the roof or the upper side of an outside wall.*
- The wiring runs through conduit, which is secured to the side of the house, and into the **meter base**.
- From the meter, the electrical current goes to a distribution system, which is a **fuse box** or a **circuit panel**.

√ **Note:** Fuses can still be purchased, but fuse boxes are no longer produced.

Amperage and Volts

The amount of **amperage (amps)** of electricity available to a house is determined by the amount of power the electric company *transmits to the house*. The amps may be determined by looking at the **electric meter** on the house; most modern meters have the designation "CL200," which means they are rated for up to a 200-amp service. The higher the amperage of the house, the more electrical devices can be used.

Sidebar

Houses built post WWII typically had 60-amp service. Currently, many lenders will not accept 60-amp electrical systems, nor will some insurance companies. Those service panels must be upgraded to 100 amp (minimum), 150 amp, or 200 amp. Electricians are likely to recommend 200 amp as that is the standard today.

Often, people mistakenly conclude that if a house has a 200-amp breaker panel (box), the house has 200-amp service. However, 200-amp panels have been installed in houses that have only 100, or even 60-amp service. For example, this photo shows the meter in the basement, directly above the breaker box. Although this is a 200-amp box, the service being provided to this house from the power company is only 60 amps, which may not supply enough power for the inhabitants of the house.

Figure 7.1: 200 Amp Box in House with 60 Amp Service
Photo Courtesy of Melanie J. McLane

A **volt** is *a measure of electric potential*. For most electrical appliances, 110 volt power is needed. But for electric ranges, large air conditioners, large tools, clothes dryers, and the like, the requirement is 220 volts. Sometimes, these large electrical appliances are directly wired into the electrical system, instead of plugging them into a **pigtail**, *a large 220-volt outlet*. The pigtail allows the appliance to be easily disconnected from the power in the event of a repair or an emergency.

Grounding Electrical Systems

Why are electrical systems grounded?

- One reason is to act as overvoltage protection. Lightning, contact with a higher voltage line, or a power surge can all send dangerously high voltages into the house's electrical system. Electricity seeks the shortest path to the earth, so grounding provides a direct path into the ground. The most common method is to install a **grounding rod** into the ground.

- Grounding also prevents accidents and damage to electrical devices. An electrical event inside a house could electrocute residents, blow out electronics, or melt the panel and wires in the house.

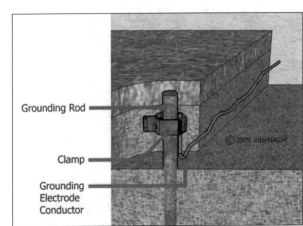

Figure 7.2: Grounding Rod Diagram; Image Courtesy of InterNACHI

√ **Caution:** Some older homes have **nob-and-tube** wiring, which is very dangerous in that it lacks grounding, as seen in this photo. As this type of wiring is considered unsafe, it is recommended that the electrical system be upgraded.

Figure 7.3: Nob and Tube Wiring
Photo Courtesy of Melanie J. McLane

In addition to electrical systems, individual outlets can be grounded as well. This is done with **GFCI (Ground Fault Circuit Interrupter)** receptacles, sometimes called 'three prong' outlets. Note that all three prong outlets are grounded, but not all are GFCI. The GFCI shuts off an electric power circuit the moment it detects current is flowing through an unintended path, such as water. GFCI receptacles are required by code in all new installations in kitchens, bathrooms, unfinished basements, crawl spaces, and outdoor receptacles.

Figure 7.4: GFCI Receptacle

√ **Note:** FHA requires GFCI receptacles for outlets nearest to the sinks in kitchens and baths.

Dangerous Situations

There are many dangerous issues with home wiring. Let's look at some of these.

Overcrowded Circuit Panel

Inside the **circuit panel** are numbered **circuit breakers**, plus a large main breaker, usually at the top or the bottom, which turns off all the power in the house. The purpose of a circuit breaker is to interrupt the current flow when an electrical issue is detected. A series of outlets in the house are connected to a specific circuit breaker in the panel; for example, all living room outlets are connected to one; all master bedroom outlets are connected to another, and so forth. Further, major appliances and equipment, such as a water heater and furnace, will each be connected to a circuit breaker. Every circuit breaker should be clearly labeled with the room, appliances, or equipment connected to it, so that if repairs are needed, the power can be turned off to a particular area.

Electrical codes vary by location, but most require that certain large appliances and equipment be connected to a designated circuit breaker (primarily ones that require a 220 line and have 240 volts). Circuits should *not* be overloaded—that is, having too many items connected to them. Doing so can exceed the limits of the circuit breaker, which causes it to snap open (trip) and shut down the circuit and everything it services. Here is a photo of an overcrowded panel.

Sometimes, empty space is available in the panel, which allows the homeowner to add additional circuits to power other electrical devices, or a home addition. The more circuits the system has, the less likely circuits will overload and trip.

Figure 7.5: Overcrowded Circuit Box
Photo Courtesy of Greg Hancock, Hancock Home Inspections

Electrical 'Handyman'

Frequently in older homes, there is a mixture of wiring, much like with plumbing. Handymen fix and add things, but often do not completely replace what's needed.

Here is a photo of a house with old nob and tube wiring that has been spliced, with obvious repairs using red and black electrical tape. To the far right is newer wiring. Most home inspectors would have issues with this electrical wiring.

Figure 7.6: Old Nob and Tube Wiring
Photo Courtesy of Melanie J. McLane

Some houses still use **fuses**, or very old electrical systems. In this photo is a fuse based system with no cover on the box, dangling wires (notice the loose ones at the upper right of the box), and the paper tags obviously are not to code. This system was installed by a handyman. There was subsequently an electrical fire in this house, which fortunately did not harm any of the residents and was extinguished before it caused significant damage. Afterwards, the house was rewired.

Figure 7.7: Owner Installed Electrical System
Photo Courtesy of Melanie J. McLane

> ### Sidebar
>
> *In older homes when there was an electrical overload, fuses would 'blow.' People would replace blown fuses with a penny, which conveniently fit into the space, and being copper, conducted electricity, so the electrical system would still work. Of course, when an overload occurred again, the penny would not 'blow' and often resulted in the house catching fire!*

Federal Pacific Stab-Lok Panel Box

One well known dangerous home wiring system is the **Federal Pacific Stab-Lok** panel box, as seen in this photo.

Federal Pacific boxes are still in houses, as millions were sold from the 1950s through the early 1980s.

The engineering of the Stab-Lok breakers created a unique problem of the circuits *not* breaking when they should. The circuits were defective from the start, and the history of the sale of the company supports deceit within the business.

Figure 7.8: Federal Pacific Stab-Lok Panel Box
Photo Courtesy of Greg Hancock, Hancock Home Inspections

In 1979, Reliance Electric acquired Federal Pacific; shortly thereafter, Exxon acquired Reliance.

A lawsuit for $345 million was filed by Reliance against the liquidating trust that arranged the sale of Federal Pacific, and in the lawsuit, Reliance stated that "improper and deceptive practices were employed for many years to secure UL (Underwriting Labs) listings for Federal Pacific's circuit protective products." As a result of the lawsuit, the Consumer Product Safety Commission (CPSC) investigated, and found an abnormally high failure rate. The lawsuits drug on, but finally, in 2002 in New Jersey (headquarters of Federal Pacific), a superior court judge issued a summary judgment, which affirmed that Federal Pacific had knowingly violated the Consumer Fraud Safety Act in New Jersey. Federal Pacific had hired inspectors and attorneys of their own, and had gotten experts to claim their systems are safe.

√ **Caution:** The consensus among home inspectors and electricians is that any Federal Pacific box *should be replaced*.

Aluminum Wiring

Another dangerous electrical issue in houses is **aluminum wiring**, which came into use when copper increased dramatically in price. The issue is that aluminum wiring becomes defective much more quickly than copper, and as it deteriorates, it becomes dangerous. Here is a quote from the Consumer Products Safety Commission (CPSC):

"Homes wired with aluminum wire manufactured before 1972 ['old technology' aluminum wire] are 55 times more likely to have one or more connections reach "Fire Hazard Conditions" than is a home wired with copper."

The negative attributes of aluminum as a metal that make it dangerous for wiring include:

- Higher electrical resistance, which requires aluminum conductors be of a larger diameter than would be needed for copper

- Less ductile, which means that it will break more easily after being bent; copper, by comparison, is very ductile

- Galvanic corrosion can occur when it is exposed to moisture and dissimilar metals
- Oxidation, which causes deterioration to the outer surface—as it deteriorates, it can present a fire hazard
- Greater malleability, which means that it is very sensitive to compression, so if a screw is overtightened on an aluminum wire, it will continue to deform even after the pressure is removed; this can create a loose connection
- Greater thermal expansion and contraction with temperature changes—because of this, it is not suited for terminations found on the backs of light switches and outlets, which are known as "stab," "bayonet," or "push-in"

√ **Note:** Many insurance companies will *not* cover homes that use single strand aluminum wiring.

How to Identify Aluminum Wiring

To identify if aluminum wiring was used in a house, look for the following:

- Wiring that is a dull grey color, unlike copper, which is clearly copper colored
- Wiring in light switches and receptacles marked "CO/ALR" (copper/aluminum revised)
- In the attic, basement, or near the electrical panel, the plastic wire jacket (plastic tubing surrounding the wire) is printed or embossed with the word "Aluminum," the initials "AL", or a brand name such as "Kaiser Aluminum."

The consensus among inspectors and electricians is that the best 'fix' for aluminum wiring is removal and replacement with copper wire. However, this is expensive, so a licensed electrician should inspect it and make recommendations for repairs.

Electrical Questions

Every day, houses are sold that are not up to electrical code. That being said, here is a list of some basic things to look for:

- What is the amperage of electricity available to the house?
- Is the amperage adequate for the house?
- Are the outlets grounded?
- Are there GFCI outlets?
- Are there two-prong outlets or three prong outlets?
- How many outlets are there per room?
- Are there any floor outlets? Floor outlets must have covers to comply with code.
- Are there any open junction boxes?
- Is there any nob and tube wiring?
- Does the panel box appear full?
- Is the panel box clearly labeled?
- Is there any evidence of fraying or loose wires?
- Is the service cable on the outside of the house intact?

Questions to typically ask the homeowner include:

- Have you ever had any problems with the electrical system in your house?

- Have you ever had an electrical fire?

- Do your circuit switches trip, or if you have fuses, do they blow?

- How many outlets do you have, and where are they?

- Are there any outlets or fixtures that do not work?

- Are you aware of any old nob and tube, or aluminum wiring in your house?

- Are there sub-panels elsewhere on the property?

Chapter Summary

1. Electricity for household use began in the 1800s. Notable contributors to household electric include Joseph Swan, Thomas Edison, H. J. Rogers, Nikola Tesla, William Stanley, Jr., and Charles Proteus Steinmetz.

2. In the 1900s, several electrical appliances for the home emerged: Vacuum cleaner, washing machine, refrigerator, and dishwasher.

3. Electricity begins at the power plant and is transmitted through a distribution system or power grid. The power goes to an underground or overhead wire into the meter base on the house. From there, it goes into a fuse box or circuit panel.

4. Amperage (amps) of electricity available is determined by the amount of power the electric company is transmitting to the house.

5. A volt is a measure of electric potential. Most electrical appliances require 110 volts, and larger appliances and tools require 220 volts.

6. Electrical systems must be grounded, with a grounding rod, as overvoltage protection and to prevent accidents and damage to electrical devices.

7. GFCI (Ground Fault Circuit Interrupter) receptacles shut off electric power circuits the moment current flows through an unintended path, such as water. FHA requires GFCI receptacles for outlets nearest to the sinks in kitchens and baths.

8. Dangerous electrical situations include overcrowded circuit panels, improper installation of wiring, faulty panels such as the Federal Pacific Stab-Lok panel box, and aluminum wiring.

Chapter Quiz

1. *Which statement about electricity is TRUE?*

   a. By 1900, most Americans had electricity in their houses.

   b. Nikola Tesla advocated the use of direct current.

   c. Thomas Edison pioneered all advances in electrical engineering.

   d. The world's first central power plant was the Pearl Street Station.

2. *Initial power stations, such as the Edison Pearl Street Station,*

   a. could only power a limited number of houses, in close proximity to the station.

   b. produced enough electricity to power thousands of homes.

   c. used transformers to send electricity long distances.

   d. were all powered by hydroelectric power.

3. *Which statement about inventions is TRUE?*

   a. George Westinghouse invented the first AC system.

   b. Joseph Swan invented the first light bulb.

   c. William Hoover invented the electric vacuum cleaner.

   d. William Stanley invented the first washing machine.

4. *Which of the following inventions was by a female?*

   a. washing machine

   b. dishwasher

   c. refrigerator

   d. vacuum cleaner

5. *For large electrical appliances such as a range or clothes dryer, what is the voltage required?*

   a. 220

   b. 210

   c. 200

   d. 110

6. *Which type of wiring is considered most dangerous?*

   a. aluminum

   b. aluminum-copper

   c. copper

   d. nob and tube

7. *The purpose of a grounding rod is to*

   a. bring current from the ground to the circuit panel.

   b. ground the electric meter.

   c. provide a path for excess electricity to enter the ground.

   d. support the mast.

8. *What is the issue with Federal Pacific Stab-Lok Panels?*

   a. The circuits trip constantly, when there is no problem at all.

   b. The circuits will not trip, causing a fire hazard.

   c. Pennies placed in the fuse box would 'blow' fuses, resulting in house fires.

   d. They contain aluminum wires.

9. *Which is NOT an issue with aluminum wiring?*

   a. higher electric resistance

   b. galvanic corrosion can occur

   c. greater thermal expansion

   d. more expensive than copper wiring

10. *Amperage of electricity available to a house is determined by*

    a. the amount of direct current available.

    b. the amount of power the electric company transmits.

    b. the amperage in the breaker panel.

    d. the type of electrical system installed.

Chapter 8:

Energy Efficiency and Green Features

Chapter Introduction

In this chapter, we will discuss the purpose of building energy efficient features into homes. We will examine the various types of insulation used in homes as well as the energy efficiency of windows. Further, we will explore two primary methods used to evaluate energy efficiency. Finally, we will end this chapter with a discussion on green certification programs.

Chapter Objectives

After completing this chapter, students will be able to:

- Explain the reasons buyers desire green features in their homes.
- Identify the major types of insulation.
- Describe energy efficiency of windows.
- Explain the methods used to determine energy efficiency in homes.
- Describe green certification programs.

Attic Baffles A building product made of strips of a foam product that is installed on the inside of the attic roof, which allows air to circulate from the soffit through the attic. This prevents the insulation from making the house too air tight, causing indoor air pollution and moisture problems. Also called **Rafter Vents**, **Channel Vents**, **Vent Chutes**, and other names.

Energy Efficient Mortgage (EEM) A mortgage that credits a home's energy efficiency in the mortgage itself. EEMs give borrowers the opportunity to finance cost-effective, energy-saving measures as part of a single mortgage and stretch debt-to-income qualifying ratios on loans, thereby allowing borrowers to qualify for a larger loan amount and a better and more energy-efficient home.

Energy Guide Labels The yellow stickers affixed to products to advise the consumer of both the projected energy consumption of that particular product, and the average energy consumption for other products like it.

ENERGY STAR One of the rating systems available to evaluate homes for energy efficiency. ENERGY STAR raters are RESNET approved.

Green 1) A word widely and loosely used to describe the use, in construction, of renewable materials; 2) non-toxic materials, and sometimes locally produced materials, usually with an energy efficient component.

Greenwashing The practice of touting a product or program as environmentally friendly, when in fact, it is not.

(continued on page 101)

Energy Efficiency and Green

Home buyers are interested in the energy efficiency of a house to save money and for other reasons. Today, many are concerned about green features. 'Green' means different things to different people and can be misinterpreted, much like the word 'organic or 'natural.' We define **green** as *the use of renewable materials and energy; products that are produced with a minimum of waste, with consideration given to the cost of harvesting and transporting them; products that are considered safe for use in housing, and which do not contain VOCs, and known carcinogens, such as asbestos or lead.*

Most buyers do not want to use more energy or deplete more of the planet's natural resources than is necessary. For example, the home pictured here, in the Bethlehem PA area, was built using only materials manufactured within 70 miles of the home, meaning that very little fossil fuel energy was used to get the materials to the site.

Figure 8.1: Home Built with Local Materials
Photo Courtesy of Ruhmel Builders

Then, there are buyers who seek green houses to avoid VOCs (Volatile Organic Chemicals) and other building materials that can aggravate existing health conditions, such as allergies or asthma, or create other health issues. For instance, in the past few years, buyers have shown a strong preference for hardwood flooring to avoid chemicals, dust mites, and other allergens in carpeting.

Even houses that are not 'green' by today's standards may have energy efficient features. Recall in the chapter on windows and doors, we discussed storm windows, thermal windows, and the U-value of windows, as well as the benefit of insulated doors. As with almost everything, as the technology has improved, insulation, windows, and doors have become more energy efficient.

Insulation Materials

The major types of insulation include:

- **Blanket batts and rolls** – Made from fiberglass, mineral wool, plastic, or natural fibers (including blue jeans). This is applied to unfinished walls, ceilings, and floors and is fitted between studs, joists, and beams.

- **Foam board and rigid foam** – Made from polystyrene, polyisocyanurate, and polyurethane. This can be used on unfinished walls, including foundation walls, floors, ceilings, and unvented low-slope roofs. When applied to the interior, the foam must be covered with 1/2" drywall or another similar material approved for fire safety. If applied to the exterior, it must be covered with a weatherproof product.

- **Insulating concrete forms (ICFs)** – Foam forms (blocks, panels, and planks) that are used for construction of walls, floors, or roofs. IFC systems are made with interlocking modular units (similar to 'Lego' blocks) that are dry-stacked (no mortar) and filled with concrete.

- **Blown-in or loose-fill** – Insulation material that is usually 'blown-in' using special equipment or poured into a cavity. The materials used are cellulose, fiberglass, and mineral wool. It is a popular way to insulate existing homes, to fill uninsulated areas and to add insulation to places not insulated previously, which may be irregularly shaped or have obstructions in the way.

- **Foam beads** or **liquid foam** – Made from polystyrene, cementitious, phenolic, polyisocyanurate, or polyurethane. Foam beads or liquid foam can be applied to unfinished walls and are used in new construction and major renovations. Like blown-in insulation, foam is a good solution if the insulation needs to go into an irregular space or around a barrier.

- **Reflective system** – Insulation made of foil-faced kraft paper, plastic film, polyethylene bubbles, or even cardboard. It is used in unfinished walls and fitted between studs, joists, and beams.

- **Rigid fibrous or fiber** – Insulation made of fiberglass or mineral wool. It is used in ducts in unconditioned spaces and often for places that must withstand high temperatures.

- **Attic baffle or rafter vents** – A foam product that is installed on the inside of the attic roof, which allows air to circulate from the soffit through the attic. Without them, the house would be too tight, causing indoor air quality problems as well as moisture problems.

Figure 8.2: Attic Baffles in Roof
Photo Courtesy of Clark McLane

Insulation Resistance Factor

An *insulating material's resistance to conductive heat flow is measured or rated in terms of its thermal resistance* or **R-value**. The higher the R-value, the greater the insulating effectiveness. For example, R-21 is more resistant than R-13.

This table provides insulation recommendations for various parts of a house based on climate zone and fuel used for heating:

					Insulation Recommendations				
Zone	Gas	Heat Pump	Fuel Oil	Electric	Attic	Cathedral Ceiling	Cavity	Insulation Sheathing	Floor
1	•	•	•	•	R30 to R49	R22 to R38	R13 to R15	None	R13
2	•	•	•		R30 to R60	R22 to R38	R13 to R15	None	R13
				•	R30 to R60	R22 to R38	R13 to R15	None	R19 - R25
3	•	•	•		R30 to R60	R22 to R38	R13 to R15	None	R25
				•	R30 to R60	R22 to R38	R13 to R15	R2.5 to R5	R25
4	•	•	•		R38 to R60	R30 to R38	R13 to R15	R2.5 to R6	R25 - R30
				•	R38 to R60	R30 to R38	R13 to R15	R5 to R6	R25 - R30
5	•	•	•		R38 to R60	R30 to R38	R13 to R15	R5 to R6	R25 - R30
				•	R38 to R60	R30 to 60	R13 to R21	R2.5 to R6	R25 - R30
6	•	•	•	•	R49 to R60	R30 to 60	R13 to R21	R5 to R6	R25 - R30
7	•	•	•	•	R49 to R60	R30 to 60	R13 to R21	R5 to R6	R25 - R30
8	•	•	•	•	R49 to R60	R30 to 60	R13 to R21	R5 to R6	R25 - R30

Figure 8.3: Insulation Recommendations
Source: U.S. Department of Energy

Energy Efficiency of Windows

For energy efficient windows, the **U–factor** *measures thermal conductivity in windows.* Unlike R-values, the lower the number, the better the insulating capability. Here are some examples of U-factors:

- Single pane, aluminum frame: 1.30
- Double pane, 1/2" air space: .81

Clearly, in the example above, the single pane window is the least efficient; some homes still have these, although they usually have storm windows. The double pane or triple pane thermal windows are much more energy efficient.

In thermal windows, two gases are commonly used between the panes as insulation:

- **Argon** – Cheaper and the most commonly used gas
- **Krypton** – Provides better insulating properties as it is a dense gas, but is more expensive

Thermal windows have a low-e (low-emissivity) glass with a coating of clear, microscopic metal oxide. **Low-e** *reflects some rays (long-wavelength) of the sun, but allows others (short-wavelength) to penetrate.* So, in winter, it brings in the warmth from the sun and keeps the warmth in the house.

Energy Efficiency Assessments

Energy efficiency assessments of houses are performed by a variety of entities:

- A qualified home energy auditor
- A home inspector (many offer energy audits for an additional cost)
- Electric utility companies (for free or for a very reasonable fee)

√ **Note:** A routine whole-house energy assessment includes an insulation check and identifies areas that are in need of air sealing.<end>

Determining Energy Efficiency

Two non-invasive methods to check the energy efficiency of a house are:

- Thermal (infrared) imaging test
- Blower door test

An **infrared thermal camera** is used for the thermal imaging test and can reveal 'hot' and 'cold' spots in a house, as well as water infiltration and leaks. These cameras are a valuable tool as they can:

- Detect variations in temperature,
- Pinpoint where insulation is missing or inadequate, and
- Pinpoint water leaks behind walls.

Use of an infrared camera is not just limited to older houses; owners of new homes, after experiencing 'cold spots,' have discovered that insulation that was in the specs for the house was never installed!

A **blower door test** is an *energy test performed on a house to determine the airtightness of a house.*

1. The test is performed by installing a powerful fan into the frame of an exterior door.
2. When the fan is activated, it pulls the air out of the house, which lowers the interior air pressure.
3. Then, the higher outside air pressure flows in, revealing unsealed cracks and openings.
4. A pressure gauge measures the differences in air pressure.

√ **Note:** A blower door test should be calibrated. The calibration measures the amount of air pulled out of the building, and helps to identify how much air is leaking and where.

Houses that leak air consume more energy and may have draft and moisture issues, which can cause poor indoor air quality.

RESNET

The **Residential Energy Services Network (RESNET)** was founded in 1995 as an *independent, non-profit organization that helps homeowners reduce the cost of their utility bills by making their homes more energy efficient.*

RESNET developed the **Home Energy Rating System (HERS) Index**, or **HERS Index**, which is *a nationally recognized scoring system for measuring a home's energy performance.* The index is used to demonstrate a home's total energy efficiency. Various green certification programs use the HERS Index, including ENERGY STAR and LEED.

A certified HERS Rater inspects and tests the homes energy features. The information is entered into the rating software, which issues a HERS Index score. The lower the score, the more energy efficient the home, thus saving on energy costs.

The HERS Index uses a scoring system from 150 down to 0. A standard new home has a score of 100. Each point on the scale represents 1% of energy efficiency. Given this:

- A home with a score of 130 is 30% less energy efficient than a standard new home.
- A home with a score of 70 is 30% more energy efficient than a standard new home.
- A home with a score of 0 is a **Net Zero Energy Home**, which means it *produces as much energy through renewable sources as it consumes.*

The U.S. Department of Energy has determined that a typical resale home scores 130 on the HERS Index.

√ **Note:** For an appraiser, the HERS Index Score is a reference point that is quantifiable, such as, "This house has a HERS rating of 50, and comparable #1 has a HERS rating of 75."

HERS ratings are used by the federal government for verification of a building's energy performance, as well as for **Energy Efficient Mortgages (EEMs)**. **EEMs** are *mortgages available for energy efficient homes.* They allow the borrower to borrow more on the mortgage, because the cost of energy use in the house is considered. They can also be used in rehab loans, such as the FHA programs, to finance purchase of a home and adding energy efficient features.

Green Certification Programs

Green certification programs were developed to promote sustainable practices in the building industry. The major players in green certification programs are:

- ENERGY STAR
- NAHB (National Association of Home Builders)
- LEED (Leadership in Energy & Environmental Design)

These programs serve to educate consumers by providing ratings based on green building features in homes.

ENERGY STAR

ENERGY STAR is a U.S. Environmental Protection Agency (EPA) voluntary program that helps businesses and individuals save money and protect our climate through superior energy efficiency. The ENERGY STAR program was established by the EPA in 1992, under the authority of the Clean Air Act Section 103(g).

ENERGY STAR ratings are available for both new and existing housing. ENERGY STAR specifically considers:

- Effective insulation
- High performance windows
- Tight construction and ducts
- Efficient heating and cooling equipment
- Efficient products

Because ENERGY STAR uses an independent third party to rate houses, it is more reliable than the builder simply stating that the house is 'green' or 'energy efficient.' And ENERGY STAR, by a wide margin, *tests and certifies more homes than any other program.*

RESNET ENERGY STAR

A RESNET ENERGY STAR rating is the minimum code compliance, with respect to energy efficiency for 16 states. Home Energy Raters can do a physical inspection of an existing home, or use energy-modeling software to estimate the future energy use. This yields a projected HERS rating, based on heating, cooling, water heating, and lighting. If there are on-site power systems, such as solar, they are part of the evaluation. If upgrades are needed to be plans to ensure that the house meets ENERGY STAR performance guidelines, these are identified. Over a conventional home, ENERGY STAR homes should reduce energy use by at least 15% in climate zones 1 to 5 and a 20% savings is the minimum in northern tier climate states, which are zones 6 to 8. Because of specific climates and codes, the EPA allows California, Hawaii, and the Pacific Northwest to use their own locally developed energy codes.

√ **Caution:** Because ENERGY STAR ratings are also used for appliances, beware of builders and others who put high efficiency appliances in a house and then call it an "ENERGY STAR" house. This is called **greenwashing**, which is *the practice of touting a product or program as environmentally friendly, when in fact, it is not.*

NAHB National Green Building Standards

The **National Association of Home Builders (NAHB)** and the **International Code Council (ICC)** have developed and published the *NAHB National Green Building Standards*. These standards apply to single, multi-unit, residential remodeling, and site development projects, and are customized for different parts of the United States.

NAHB **originally** only required that *a representative sampling (15%) of the same models of houses built by the same builder* be subject to a physical review. In theory, this saves time and money; in practice, sub-contractors do not always follow the plans and specs. The **new** NAHB National Green Program requires that *100% of the houses be tested.*

NAHB uses a point-based rating system for green building standards. Energy requirements are tied to the International Energy Conservation Code (IECC), providing builders with a mechanism to meet code and earn points for green buildings. Based on the number of points earned, NAHB awards four levels of certification to home builders (ranked below from lowest to highest):

- Bronze
- Silver
- Gold
- Emerald

One of the interesting requirements at the **Gold level** for NAHB is that the owner gets an 'owner's manual' from the builder. This contains:

- Basic information about maintenance and operation.
- Certification level of the home.
- Warranty manuals.
- Community information about recycling, public transportation, and other features.
- Explanation of the benefits of using compact fluorescent light bulbs (or LEDs).
- Tips for conserving energy and water use.

> √ **Note:** It is now a common practice among some home inspectors to provide buyers with this type of manual, including directions for routine maintenance and time frames (e.g., "clean the gutters and downspouts twice a year," or "check the furnace filter and replace it monthly," etc.).

LEED

LEED (Leadership in Energy Efficiency & Design) *is an internationally recognized green building certification system and standard.* It delivers third-party verification that a space was designed and built using best-in-class strategies to address its entire life cycle. This program is approved by the United States Green Building Council (USGBC).

LEED ratings are available for:

- Residential
- New builds
- Re-habs
- Tenant build outs
- Commercial
- Institutional

USGBC takes into account the entire building project from start to finish, which includes:

- Site and site design, which includes building placement
- Energy efficiency of the building and component parts
- Sustainability
- Conservation of natural resources
- Reduced waste during building process
- Reduction of greenhouse gases

Projects pursuing LEED certification earn points across several areas that address sustainability issues. Based on the number of points achieved, a project then receives one of four LEED rating levels (ranked below from lowest to highest):

- Certified
- Silver
- Gold
- Platinum

As an 'entry level' requirement, a house has to have a **HERS score** of **85 or less** to be considered for LEED certification.

LEED ratings are more expensive to obtain, and for this reason, more builders use either NAHB or ENERGY STAR.

Inspecting for Energy Efficiency

It's important for a real estate professional to:

- Inspect the home first for discernible energy efficient features.

- Ask the owners about energy efficient and green features, including typical energy costs.

- If the owners state their home is a 'green' house, inquire as to whether one of the major rating groups has rated the house, and if so, when was it done, and what is the rating.

- Ask to see energy bills, find out when systems were installed, and determine what the physical life of the system is estimated to be.

Chapter Summary

1. Home buyers are interested in energy efficient 'green' houses to save money, to use fewer natural resources, and to avoid materials that can cause health issues.

2. There are many types of insulation: Blanket batts and rolls, foam board and rigid foam, insulating concrete forms (ICFs), blown-in or loose-fill, foam beads or liquid foam, reflective system, rigid fibrous or fiber, and attic baffles or rafter vents.

3. An insulating material's resistance to conductive heat flow is measured or rated in terms of its thermal resistance or R-value. Higher R-values provide more efficiency.

4. Energy efficiency in windows is measured by the U-factor. Lower U-factor numbers mean better efficiency.

5. Argon and krypton gases are used in thermal windows. Argon gas is most commonly used due to being cheaper than krypton, but has less insulating properties. Thermal windows have low-e glass that controls the passage of sunlight through them.

6. A home energy efficiency assessment can be performed by a qualified home energy auditor, a home inspector, or an electric utility company.

7. Two methods for testing energy efficiency in homes are the thermal (infrared) image test and the blower door test. An infrared thermal camera can reveal hot and cold spots and water infiltration and leaks. A blower door test checks for airtightness.

8. RESNET (Residential Energy Services Network) developed the Home Energy Rating System (HERS) Index, which is used to demonstrate a home's total energy efficiency. Various green certification programs use the HERS Index. HER ratings are also used for Energy Efficient Mortgages (EEMs).

9. Three main players offering green certification programs are ENERGY STAR, NAHB (National Association of Home Builders), and LEED (Leadership in Energy Efficiency & Design). These programs use point-based rating systems.

10. ENERGY STAR certifies more homes than any other program.

11. NAHB and the ICC (International Code Council) developed and published the *NAHB National Green Building Standard*.

12. LEED is approved by the United States Green Building Council (USGBC).

Chapter Quiz

1. **Which is the most common gas found between panes in thermal windows?**

   a. argon
   b. helium
   c. kryptonite
   d. radon

2. **With respect to the U-value of windows,**

   a. the higher the U-value, the higher the energy efficiency.
   b. the lower the U-value, the higher the energy efficiency.
   c. the lower the U-value, the more likely the window is to leak.
   d. windows are not rated using U-values.

3. **A buyer is considering purchasing an older home, but is concerned about the energy use. Which of the following would be MOST useful to the buyer?**

   a. all-inclusive energy audit, including an infrared camera use and a blower door test
   b. evaluation of the current owner's utility bills
   c. online review of the house via website
   d. visual inspection by the appraiser or agent of the property

4. **Which type of insulation would BEST be suited to an area where the insulation needs to go around existing barriers and fill an irregular space?**

   a. batts
   b. blown in
   c. ICFs
   d. rigid foam

5. **A buyer can choose from the following insulation and window packages from the builder. Which is the MOST energy efficient?**

   a. R-19 walls; R-22 ceilings; double pane low-E windows with a U-value rating of .65
   b. R-12 walls; R-24 ceilings; double pane low-E windows with a U-value rating of .75
   c. R-19 walls; R-30 ceilings; triple pane, low-E windows with a U-value rating of .67
   d. R-19 walls; R-30 ceilings; triple pane, low-E windows with a U-value rating of .41

6. **Which of the following green certification programs certifies more homes for energy efficiency?**

   a. EEM
   b. ENERGY STAR
   c. LEED
   d. NAHB

7. **A zero net energy home**

   a. is an impossibility.
   b. is theoretically possible, yet impractical.
   c. produces all of the energy it consumes.
   d. requires no energy to run it.

8. **Which entity does NOT perform energy efficiency assessments of homes?**

   a. electric utility company
   b. energy auditor
   c. environmental protection agency
   d. home inspector

9. **Which is the top NAHB certification level awarded to green home builders?**

   a. bronze
   b. emerald
   c. gold
   d. silver

10. **An infrared thermal camera CANNOT detect**

    a. air leaks.
    b. cold spots.
    c. hot spots.
    d. water leaks.

11. **Which is NOT a primary reason that buyers want 'green' features in their homes?**

    a. avoid health reasons
    b. higher resell value
    c. save money
    d. use fewer natural resources

Chapter 9:
Environmental Issues

Chapter Introduction

In this chapter, we will discuss environmental issues that could be discovered in houses. We will examine the causes of hazardous indoor air quality and the risks to occupants. As well, we will explain how indoor pollutants and contaminants can be mitigated.

Chapter Objectives

After completing this chapter, students will be able to:

- Identify causes of indoor air quality by occupants.
- Describe common indoor environmental hazards and their risks.
- Explain testing methods and remedies for indoor environmental hazards.

Asbestos A fibrous material derived from a naturally occurring group of minerals; used in building materials for both its natural insulating properties and fire resistance.

Carbon Monoxide A natural byproduct of fuel combustion; a colorless, odorless gas released as fuel sources break down to produce heat.

Encapsulation The process of applying a sealant to asbestos-containing material, which penetrates the material's surface, preventing the release of the dangerous fibers.

Friable When asbestos, or the material containing asbestos, crumbles, pulverizes, or reduces to powder by moderate pressure.

Lead A mineral used in pipes and paint, as well as other products, including glazes on ceramic tiles. In sufficient quantities, lead is carcinogenic.

Radon A naturally occurring radioactive gas that emanates from rocks, soil, and water due to the decay of uranium.

Urea-formaldehyde A thermosetting synthetic resin made from urea and formaldehyde; used in the manufacturing of building materials, and home products such as particleboard, plywood paneling, carpeting, and ceiling tiles.

Volatile Organic Compounds (VOCs) Gases emitted from certain solids or liquids; organic chemicals found in many household products.

Indoor Air Quality

Indoor air quality of a house can be much worse than outside when:

- The house is sealed too tightly, which prevents fresh air from entering the home. Most experts agree that about half of all indoor air pollution is caused by **inadequate ventilation**.

- The inside air is unhealthy.

Occupants can create unhealthy indoor air quality by:

- Smoking cigars, cigarettes, or pipes.

- Using or bringing inside products that contain volatile organic compounds (VOCs); e.g., paints, solvents, wood preservatives, aerosol sprays, cleaners, disinfectants, air fresheners, clothes from the drycleaner.

- Using or bringing inside pesticides, or storing them in an attached or built-in garage.

- Using a wood stove, an unvented gas or kerosene heater, or a gas fireplace.

- Not getting rid of excessive moisture, thus creating a place for mold to grow.

- Using products that contain formaldehyde; e.g., hardwood, plywood wall paneling, particleboard, fiberboard, some insulation, and some glues.

Symptoms of Indoor Pollution

The symptoms for most pollutants are unpleasant, including:

- Eye, nose, throat irritation
- Impaired lung function
- Bronchitis
- Lung cancer
- Flu-like symptoms
- Headaches
- Pneumonia
- Increased risk of respiratory and ear infections in children
- Loss of coordination
- Nausea
- Damage to kidneys and central nervous systems
- Cancer in humans and animals

Indoor Environmental Hazards

Indoor environmental hazards can be man-made or naturally occurring. Although there is usually a distinction between man-made and natural environmental concerns, some hazards fall into both categories. For instance, asbestos and lead occur naturally; however, the manipulation and use of these materials by man has made them potentially hazardous.

Asbestos

Asbestos is *a fibrous material derived from a naturally occurring group of minerals.* The mining and use of asbestos began in the U.S. in the late 1800s, and became more widespread during World War II. In the past, asbestos was commonly found in many building materials because of its insulating and heat- and fire-resistant properties. It was also embedded in various construction materials, such as cement and plastic, ceiling and floor tiles, and was used to insulate pipes and ductwork in older buildings. Asbestos wrapped pipes are still common, as evidenced in this photo.

Figure 9.1: Asbestos Wrapped Pipes
Photo Courtesy of Melanie J. McLane

√ **Caution:** Most experts do *not* recommend removal of asbestos around pipes; instead, they urge homeowners to **encapsulate** it. Removing it makes the asbestos particles **friable**, and once airborne, they are a health hazard.

Typical procedures to collect samples of asbestos (or other airborne contaminants) include:

- **Air sampling** – Moving a determined amount of air across a filter that captures particles.
- **Bulk sampling** – A certified asbestos handler removes a small piece of the suspect material.
- **Wipe sampling** – Gathering particles from a common surface, such as the floor or countertop, by wiping the area with a piece of filter paper.

√ **Caution:** Although, collecting samples of asbestos can be done with a do-it-yourself (DIY) asbestos testing kit, it is recommended that a professional testing service be used due to the potential health hazard. Samples must be sent to a laboratory with either method; however, professional services typically receive faster results.

Lead

Until 1978, lead was added to exterior and interior paint as a drying agent and for pigmentation. Also, lead pipes and solder were commonly used in plumbing systems in homes and businesses prior to the 1930s. Products containing lead can still be found in buildings today.

Research found that digesting or inhaling lead or lead dust caused various health issues in children and adults. According to the U.S. Department of Housing and Urban Development (HUD), almost one million children in the U.S. under the age of six suffer from lead poisoning.

Common points of entry for lead:

1. **Double hung wooden windows** – found in older houses, over which aluminum storm and sash combinations have been installed. As the windows go up and down, the paint is worn away in the frame of the window, causing lead dust to settle on the sill area.

2. **Suspended tile ceilings** – found in kitchens and other rooms. For example, in one older house, every time the door opened or closed, air pressure caused the kitchen ceiling tiles to move, producing dust in the food preparation area. Ultimately, one of the children living in the house was diagnosed with lead poisoning.

3. **Metal fences** – found around play areas and vegetable gardens.

4. **Lead Pipes** – found in home plumbing and public water systems.

Lead in water or paint can only be detected through laboratory testing; however, any appraiser who sees *peeling, flaking, or chipping paint* on a home built *before* 1978 for a VA, FHA, or USDA loan must assume the paint contains lead, and call for it to be removed and repainted.

√ **Caution:** Proper handling of lead paint in the home is critical. For more information, consult the HUD publication titled *Caution: Lead Paint. Handle With Care.*

Carbon Monoxide

Carbon monoxide (CO) is *a natural byproduct of fuel combustion and is a colorless, odorless gas released as fuel sources break down to produce heat.* Thus, CO is emitted by appliances such as furnaces, space heaters, fireplaces, water heaters, and stoves. When these appliances function properly, small, regulated amounts of CO are emitted and dissipate. Unfortunately, if malfunctions occur, unacceptable levels of CO can be released. Larger amounts of CO can also be released when ventilation is inadequate. Excess carbon monoxide can lead to brain damage or even death.

Many homeowners have installed homemade stoves that do not meet code requirements and may make the house uninsurable. Here is a photo of one of these stoves.

Figure 9.2: Homemade Wood Stove
Photo Courtesy of Greg Hancock, Hancock Home Inspections

Chimney flues can be clogged with **creosote**, which forces carbon monoxide into the house.

Preventative measures include:

- All wood, coal, or gas burning stoves, fireplaces, wall units, etc., should be professionally installed and meet code requirements.

- Every home using the listed appliances should have working **carbon monoxide detectors**, as well as **smoke detectors**.

- Chimney flues should be in good shape and able to carry away all the smoke and fumes created in the house by the burning of various fossil fuels.

- A wood stove should *never* share a flue with a furnace, as shown in this photo.

Figure 9.3: Furnace and Wood Stove Sharing Flue

Radon

Radon is *a naturally occurring radioactive gas that emanates from rocks, soil, and water due to the decay of uranium.* It is the densest gas known and is odorless, colorless, and tasteless. Since it is radioactive, it has been identified as a cancer-causing agent. Lung cancer is the primary health concern of extended exposure to radon. There is also the possibility it could contribute to other health issues, such as allergies, asthma, hypertension, diabetes, and birth defects.

The presence of radon can vary from location to location, and from house to house. Points of entry for radon include:

- Private well water
- Cracks in the foundation
- A sump pump hole

The only way to determine the presence of radon is to have a test conducted. If radon is discovered, a **radon mitigation system** is fairly easy to install and generally, in most parts of the country, costs less than $2,000. Here is a photo of a system, which has a plastic pipe installed in the sump pump hole in the basement that runs up the side of the house to above the roof line. Once the radon comes into contact with the atmosphere, it dissipates immediately and is no longer a problem.

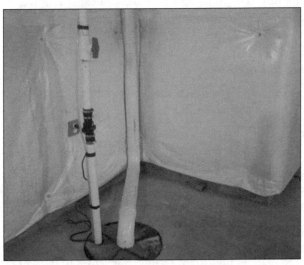

Figure 9.4: Radon Mitigation System; Photo Courtesy of Tim Tepes, Builder

Urea-Formaldehyde

Urea-formaldehyde is *a thermosetting synthetic resin made from urea and formaldehyde,* which is used in building materials and home products such as:

- Particleboard
- Plywood paneling
- Foam insulation
- Ceiling tiles
- Carpeting
- Cabinetry
- Furniture cushions
- Mattresses
- Fabric finishes
- Adhesives

The EPA regulates the use of formaldehyde and determines appropriate emission levels, especially in the construction of prefabricated and mobile homes. The EPA now recommends Urea-formaldehyde foam insulation (UFFI) not be used in residential homes because of potential health risks. Over time, the formaldehyde fumes dissipate from UFFI, so insulation installed several years ago should not pose a health risk now.

Mold

Mold is a fungus that can grow anywhere and on any organic material. In order to grow, mold requires three components:

1. Moisture
2. Oxygen
3. Food source

There are many different varieties and types of molds, but not all molds are created equal – some types, known as **mycotoxins**, are toxic and dangerous to humans. One of these types of mold is **stachybotrys**, or **black mold**, which is greenish-black in color and grows on materials with high cellulose content.

Mold can produce allergens, which can trigger reactions such as wheezing, eye and skin irritation, and a stuffy nose. For some people, mold can cause asthma attacks, chronic fatigue, digestive problems, and even neurological problems.

Mold is commonly found as a result of:

- A leaky roof that goes undetected.
- Drywall, ceiling tiles, and wood that are chronically moist. Mold can even grow behind the surface of walls or wallpaper and can actually consume the substance on which it is growing.
- Serious water damage that creates a perfect atmosphere for mold growth.
- New construction, which creates tightly sealed homes, allowing moisture to remain trapped in the home.

Detecting Environmental Issues

As a real estate professional, it's important to use your senses to detect environmental issues.

- A bad smell in the air can indicate a more serious problem, such as mold.
- Look for mold, mildew, and signs of warped wood.
- Look for older building materials such as lead pipes and asbestos ceiling tiles.
- If remodeling is detected, ask the homeowners what products were used.
- If the water has an unpleasant smell, it may still be deemed potable (fit to drink). Obviously, if the inhabitants of the house do not drink the water, that's a huge red flag!

Most importantly, *never* guess at environmental issues. Any environmental questions or concerns should be addressed by a professional home inspector or environmental engineer.

Chapter Summary

1. Indoor air quality of a house can be much worse than outside the house if the air inside is polluted. Inadequate ventilation causes about half of all indoor air pollution.

2. Homeowners contribute to indoor air pollution by smoking; using products that contain volatile organic compounds; using pesticides, using a wood stove, an unvented gas or kerosene heater, or a gas fireplace; not removing excessive moisture; and using products that contain formaldehyde.

3. Indoor environmental hazards include asbestos, lead, carbon monoxide, radon, urea-formaldehyde, and mold.

4. Asbestos was commonly used in construction materials and can be found in ceiling and floor tiles, and in insulation wrap around pipes and ductwork.

5. Lead was used in paint, pipes, and solder. Lead can also be found in drinking water.

6. Carbon monoxide can be emitted by appliances such as furnaces, space heaters, fireplaces, water heaters, and wood stoves.

7. Radon can be found in air and water. Radon is released in the air through cracks in foundations and sump pump holes. Radon in groundwater typically comes from private wells.

8. Mold can grow anywhere and on any organic material. To grow, mold needs moisture, oxygen, and a food source (e.g., drywall, wood, insulation).

Chapter Quiz

1. *Asbestos can be found in all of these EXCEPT*

   a. ceiling tiles.

   b. floor tiles.

   c. paint.

   d. wood stove installations.

2. *Which statement about radon is FALSE?*

   a. Radon does not dissipate in the air.

   b. Radon is colorless.

   c. Radon is found only in the air.

   d. Radon is odorless.

3. *The biggest concern with urea-formaldehyde is it*

   a. has a very long half-life.

   b. is colorless and odorless.

   c. is a lightweight gas that can permeate most objects.

   d. was used in foam insulation.

4. *All of the following are sources of lead poisoning; however, _____ is the most common source of lead poisoning in children.*

   a. lead paint that is flaking, peeling, and produces dust

   b. lead pipes supplying water

   c. lead solder joining lead pipes

   d. lead products such as dishes and toys

5. *Carbon monoxide is emitted from*

   a. appliances.

   b. building materials.

   c. foam insulation.

   d. well water.

6. *Which is the most common contributor to poor indoor air quality?*

   a. aerosol propellants

   b. cigarette or cigar smoke

   c. mold

   d. poor ventilation

7. *A _____ should never share a flue with a furnace, because the flue can be clogged by creosote, which will force carbon _____ into the house.*

   a. oil furnace / dioxide

   b. oil furnace / monoxide

   c. wood stove / dioxide

   d. wood stove / monoxide

8. *Many experts recommend that pipes wrapped with intact asbestos should be*

   a. encapsulated.

   b. ignored.

   c. unwrapped.

   d. wet down and scraped.

9. *Organic chemicals that create gases that are dangerous to health are known as*

   a. friable organic compounds.

   b. half-life organic compounds.

   c. variable organic compounds.

   d. volatile organic compounds.

10. *Mold requires all these components EXCEPT*

    a. a food source.

    b. moisture.

    c. oxygen.

    d. sunlight.

Chapter 10
Design and Style

Chapter Introduction

In this chapter, we will discuss the design and style of houses and examine the commonalities and differences among them. In addition, we discuss proper layout for houses and how designs have changed over time. Finally, we will touch upon some appraisal terms to describe certain attributes of a house.

Chapter Objectives

After completing this chapter, students will be able to:

- Explain the difference between the terms 'design' and 'style' of houses.
- Describe various house designs.
- Describe the attributes of various house styles.
- Differentiate functional depreciation, physical depreciation, and external obsolescence.

Balusters Small posts or pillars, often decorative, in a series that support an upper rail. Also called **Spindles**.

Balustrade A rail and the row of balusters that support it. Seen on porches and staircases and found in a variety of architectural styles.

Board and Batten Siding A type of siding that has alternating wide boards and narrow wooden strips called battens.

Column A vertical post supporting a roof or other portions of a house. Columns are categorized by design: Doric, Ionic, Corinthian, Tuscan, and Composite. They are often associated with Greek Revival architecture.

Cornice The overhanging section just below the roof, and in Victorian and other architecture, an ornamental piece. The function of the cornice overhang is to protect the structure's walls. The cornice is traditionally by definition decorative.

Cresting A decorative feature at the roof line or roof ridge, often found on Victorian homes. It can be wrought iron or a balustrade.

Fenestration The arrangement of doors and windows in the facade of a building.

Gargoyle A carved or formed grotesque animal, serpent, or human usually made of stone or concrete and placed near the roof; often formed with a spout and used to divert water from buildings; can be found on churches or elaborate residential properties.

(continued on page 119)

House Design and Style

One of the questions many ask is "What is the style of the house?" Some people confuse elements of design with style, so let's define each:

- **Design** is *how a house looks and functions* (e.g., one story, two story, ranch).
- **Style** refers to *a distinctive appearance*, which is defined by the principles of the design (e.g., Cape Cod, Colonial, Victorian, Tudor).

For Example

The principle of the design of a classic, center-hall Colonial is 'balance.' The view from the front of house appears as a center front door with two windows to the left and two to the right, and five windows across the top, with the middle window centered over the front door. The façade exhibits a symmetrical fenestration—a 'balanced' arrangement of doors and windows.

Many houses have a mix of architectural styles. The house in this photo is a two-story Colonial that was built circa 1845-1850. Notice the **gingerbread** on the eave area, which is a decorative Victorian addition.

Figure 10.1: Colonial House with Victorian Addition; Photo Courtesy of Melanie J. McLane

House Designs

One-Story Houses

One-story homes are primarily ranches and bungalows, although cottages can be one story. Let's make a distinction between ranches and bungalows:

One-Story Ranch: A classic ranch house is rectangular in shape with all rooms on one floor. Usually, the common areas are at one end and the bedrooms are at the other. In the past 20-30 years, some builders have been separating the master suite from the other bedrooms by placing them at opposite ends of the house, with the common areas in the middle. Another popular design is to have two master suites, one at each end of the house.

One-Story Bungalow: Bungalows are more likely to be a square in shape. The bedrooms are aligned along one side of the house, but may open off of the living room, dining room, etc. Sometimes, there is a short hall to the bedrooms.

One-and-a-Half Story Houses

One-and-a-half story houses have a half story above the first floor, which may or may not be finished. Two that are common are the bungalow and Cape Cod/Cape Ann:

Bungalow: One-and-a-half story bungalows are similar to one-story bungalows, except they have extra bedrooms or unfinished space on the second floor. The stairway is usually enclosed.

Cape Cod/Cape Ann: Cape Cods and Cape Anns are 1-1/2 story houses, often with the distinctive dormer in the front, or a large, continuous dormer in the rear. Cape Ann houses have Gambrel roofs (four planes instead of two).

Two-Story Houses

Two-story houses span a variety of designs—from Colonial to contemporary. Older two-story homes typically have the common areas downstairs and the private areas upstairs. However, the trend for the past 20 years has been to place the master suite on the first floor, as a nod to aging buyers who are requesting this feature, so that they can **age in place**—*live in the home regardless of age, income, or ability level.*

Two-and-a-Half Story Houses

Two-and-a-half story houses can be Victorian, townhouses, or old row houses, which have a finished upper level.

This Victorian house, built circa 1889 in Williamsport, PA, has 30 rooms. Most of the rooms have different woods; e.g., cherry, bird's eye maple, mahogany, etc. It is now a law office. Notice the **turret** to the right in the photo.

Figure 10.2: Two-and-a-Half Story Victorian House
Photo Courtesy of Melanie J. McLane

Gingerbread An architectural style with lavish or superfluous ornamentation, which is associated with Victorian architecture.

Griffin A mythical animal that is half eagle and half lion; sometimes found on ornate residential structures.

Half Timber (Half Timbering) A construction method in which the external walls have exposed wood framing constructed of timber frames, with other materials such as plaster or brick filling the space between them.

Inglenook A space with a seat on either side of a large fireplace.

Muntins and Mullions The strips of wood (or other materials) separating panes of glass in a window. Muntins are the narrow horizontal and vertical bars, and mullions are larger horizontal or vertical members between adjoining windows.

Post A vertical structural support.

Quoin A block or brickwork on the corner of a building that is used for reinforcement or decorative use; usually constructed of different materials from the walls.

Spire A tapering roof, or an ornamental metal piece on top of a tower or turret.

Stucco A durable finish for exterior walls, usually composed of cement, sand, and lime; a fine plaster used for coating wall surfaces or molding into architectural decorations.

Turret A small tower on a building.

Key Terms

Split-Levels, Bi-levels, Raised Ranches

Split-level, bi-level, and raised ranch houses are all different names for houses with *more than one level.*

Split level houses can contain a number of levels but are commonly *four levels*, with short flights of stairs between each level:

1. **Basement level** – The lowest level, often unfinished, and used for mechanicals and storage.

2. **Family level** – Located a half flight up from the basement; often contains a family room, half bath, and laundry. Depending on the slope of the lot, may be open at grade level on one side, but partially below grade on the opposite.

3. **Living (main) level** – Completely above grade and contains the living room, dining room, and kitchen.

4. **Bedroom level** – Located a half flight up from the living area; contains the bedroom level.

A **bi-level** house contains *two levels.* The front door usually opens to a landing, where a half flight up is the main living level, and a half flight down is the lower level, which typically contains a family room and laundry, with potential for an extra bedroom and/or garage.

A **raised ranch** contains *two levels.* A full flight up is the top level that is raised above the ground, which contains the common and private areas. A full flight down, at grade level or slightly below grade, is the lower level, which functions much like a basement in a two-story home. It contains the family room, laundry, mechanicals, and possibly a garage.

Figure 10.3: Left, Split-level; middle, Bi-level; right, Raised Ranch

Two-Family Houses

Two-family properties may be called duplexes, doubles, or twins, depending upon the part of the country they're located in.

Figure 10.4: Two Family House

Row Houses

Row houses are *older, attached houses in a row*. They are common in large cities, especially in the Eastern United States. The row houses in this photo appear to have been added onto over time, due to the variation in styles.

Figure 10.5: Left, Row Houses with Style Variations; right, Row House with Similar Style
Photos courtesy of Greg Gross

Townhouses

Townhouses are today's versions of row houses, but are often designed with different frontages. They may be sold as condominiums, as opposed to single-family homes.

Figure 10.6: Townhouses

√ **Note:** Although row houses, townhouses, or even half doubles can be sold as single-family homes, they all share a common wall; sometimes called a **party wall**. They are found in cities, suburbs, and even small towns.

House Styles

The styles of houses vary widely, and to complicate matters, owners do not always stick to one specific style. The Victorians, in particular, were fond of mixing styles and adding architectural features that caught their fancy (e.g., spires, turrets, quoins, griffins, gargoyles).

To address this issue, Fannie Mae introduced the Uniform Appraisal Dataset (UAD) to standardize the terminology appraisers use to describe houses:

> *"The appraiser should enter an appropriate architectural design (style) type descriptor that best describes the subject property. Valid descriptions include, but are not limited to, 'Colonial,' 'Rambler,' 'Georgian,' 'Farmhouse'. Do not use descriptors such as 'brick,' '2 stories,' 'average,' 'conventional,' or 'typical' as these are not architectural styles. Design style names may vary by locality. The appraiser should report the name of the design style that is applicable within the local market area."*

> *Source: Fannie Mae and Freddie Mac, Uniform Appraisal Dataset Specification, Appendix D: Field-Specific Standardization Requirements*

√ **Note:** The housing styles in this chapter are by no means exhaustive; particular styles vary from region to region.

Federal Period Houses

The classic Federal Period house is symmetrical and typical features include:

- Flat roof, although some have pitched roofs
- Brick or frame
- Chimneys
- Windows containing small panes of glass with **muntins and mullions**

This photo shows a Federal style house in Connecticut. The roof is pitched, to accommodate the climate, which gets too much snow for a flat roof.

Figure 10.7: Federal Period House; Photo courtesy of Nana Smith

Farm Houses

Farm houses vary across the United States, but the early ones were built in New England and featured:

- Steep pitched roofs (because of the snow)
- Clapboard siding, usually painted white
- Two or more square rooms on each floor

Farm houses typically had low ceilings and small rooms. As time went on, these smaller homes were extended by constructing additional rooms at the front of the house (e.g., parlor, dining room, one or more bedrooms), with higher ceilings and more ornate woodwork.

> ### *Sidebar*
>
> *Throughout the 19th and into the beginning of the 20th centuries, funerals and wakes were held in homes. To ensure that coffins could be moved in and out, older houses had wide front, or double doors, which are still in place today. Some homes even had a separate door for taking the coffin through, due to superstitions about taking the dead through the doors that the living used.*

Stone Houses

Early Americans built houses with whatever materials were available and often relied on styles that were customary in their native countries. For example, large numbers of Germans immigrated to the eastern United States and often built houses of stone. This house dates back to the Revolutionary War era. It is stone from basement to attic, and the walls are 18" to 24" thick.

Colonial Houses

Colonial is a term used widely to describe traditional two-story houses. Many people think of Williamsburg, Virginia when they think of Colonial structures, because so many of the houses there have been preserved. Mixed with the Colonial style are other terms, such as "Greek Revival," "Saltbox," "Adams," etc.

This house, circa 1800-1820, is a Greek Revival house. Notice the standard **fenestration** design, and the **board and batten** siding, which is *a type of siding that has alternating wide boards and narrow wooden strips called battens*, as well as the ornamentation under the front windows.

Figure 10.8: German Built Stone House and Colonial Style House; Photos courtesy of the Melanie J. McLane

Colonial "Half House"

The Colonial style house was sometimes built with the hall and stairs on one side of the house, and called a "half house" by some. This style of house is referred to in local guides as both "Federal" and "Colonial."

This photo shows a Colonial "half house" built circa 1820. Notice the front entrance on the left side rather than in the center as with the 'classic' Colonial style.

Figure 10.9: Colonial "Half House"; Photo courtesy of Melanie J. McLane

Cape Cod Houses

"Cape Cod" is used somewhat generically to describe most story-and-a-half houses. The 'classic' Cape Cod has two symmetrical dormers at the front. The photo at left shows a Cape Cod without front dormers.

Cape Cods are an enduring style. Some have only one dormer in the front, such as the photo at right, built in 1957.

Figure 10.10: Left, Cape Cod Without Dormers; right, Cape Cod with One Dormer
Photos courtesy of Melanie J. McLane

Victorian Houses

The Victorians were noted for taking whatever elements of design and style suited their fancy and incorporating them into houses. Gingerbread is typical for Victorian era homes, as well as turrets, porches, bay windows, and other ornamentation.

This Victorian home features several typical Victorian style elements, including balconies, and a **cresting** of wrought iron at the roof line. The original roof was slate, which was typical for Victorian homes. (upper left, below)

Sometimes, the Victorians went overseas for inspiration. This photo, (below, lower left), shows a good example of an Italianate style villa built circa 1870. Note the cornices on the building at the roof line.

In this photo (below, upper right) several elements that were incorporated into the house; there is **half timbering** at the top floor**,** which is *a construction method in which the external walls have exposed wood framing constructed of timber frames, with other materials such as plaster or brick filling the space between them,* a turret, bay windows, pillars, and a porch.

Here's another late 19th century house (below, lower right) with different materials: A turret and even arched Gothic windows in the basement.

Figure 10.11: Upper left, Victorian House with Balconies and Cresting; lower left, Victorian Italianate Style Villa; upper right, Victorian with Turret and Other Elements; lower right, Victorian with Turret, Gothic Windows, and Other Elements; Photos courtesy of the Melanie J. McLane

Figure 10.12: Left, Tudor Style Home; right, French Normandy House
Photo courtesy of the Melanie J. McLane

Tudor Style

Tudor homes are recognizable by the mixture of half timbers and **stucco**, or a material that looks like stucco. Sometimes called *Elizabethan* homes, because of the long reign of Queen Elizabeth I, a Tudor Queen, they can be found in a number of variations and materials. The house in this photo, believed to have been built circa 1920-1930, is a Tudor style home.

French Normandy or Provincial

French Normandy or Provincial houses have a turret that is often a staircase. The exteriors are usually brick or stone, asymmetrical, and may have half timbers.

Figure 10.13: Left, Craftsman Style Home with Enclosed Porch; right, Craftsman Style Home with Open Porch, courtesy of Sue Neely Rice

Craftsman Houses

Craftsman style houses emerged during the Arts and Crafts movement, which began at the end of the Victorian era. Many Craftsman houses may have the following features:

- One-and-a-half stories
- Low-pitched gabled roofs
- Large front porches
- Exposed beams inside
- Fireplaces
- Built-in bookshelves
- Inglenooks

The photo at left is a Craftsman Style home, circa 1920. The front porch on this house has been enclosed.

The photo at right is a new Craftsman house where the porch was left open. Notice how the pillars are wider at the bottom. Each window has three vertical panes in the upper half and a solid pane of glass in the lower half. These features are very typical of Craftsman style homes.

Other House Styles

The Victorian era, characterized by large, ornate houses, gave way to more simple housing (e.g., Craftsman). By the turn of the 20th century, houses were both smaller and more practical.

Four Square

In a "four square" house, there are four rooms on each floor, one in each corner. A similar style of home can be found in the Denver area and is known locally as a "Denver Square."

Figure 10.14: Left, Four Square House, courtesy of Melanie J. McLane; right, Denver Square House, courtesy of Claire Ryder

Modern Houses

Many buyers became bored with traditional looking houses and opted for a modern look that was clean, functional, and simple. A wide variety of these homes can be seen in modern architecture. At left is a circa early 1970s house.

At right is a circa 1930 modern looking house that has a stucco exterior and awnings.

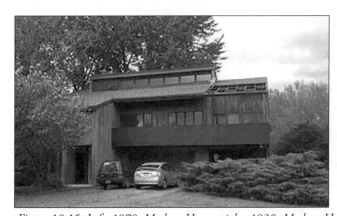

Figure 10.15: Left, 1970s Modern House; right, 1930s Modern House, Photos courtesy of Melanie J. McLane

Pre-Cut Houses

Pre-cut houses were the grandparents of modular houses. They were pre-cut offsite, and shipped in pieces for assembly onsite. There were several manufacturers of pre-cut houses.

- **Sears, Roebuck and Company** was one of the largest manufacturers of pre-cut houses. Between 1908 and 1940, Sears sold 70,000 - 75,000 of these homes. This photo is a Sears story-and-a-half bungalow with two bedrooms, living room, kitchen, bath, and dining room downstairs. Between the living room and dining room are built-in pillared half bookcases. The stairway is enclosed and leads to two bedrooms; there are no baths on the second floor.

Figure 10.16: Precut Home from Sears, Roebuck and Company, Photo courtesy of the Melanie J. McLane

- **The Aladdin Company** was founded in 1906 by brothers, Otto and William Sovereign, and was in business until 1981; thus, Aladdin was in business longer than other pre-cut home manufacturers, and sold over 75,000 homes.
- **Montgomery Ward** sold "Wardway" homes from roughly 1921 through 1931. It is reported that the Great Depression caused their demise. As was true of the Sears and Aladdin homes, Wardway homes were compact, affordable, and solid.
- **National Homes Corporation** and the **Lustron Corporation** entered the market in post-World War II. Their houses were built of enamel clad steel, with approximately 2,500 built.

Round or Octagonal Houses

Builders experimented with shape as well as style.

- **Octagonal** homes originated in the 19th century to the present.
- **Round** houses use fewer materials to enclose the same square footage as a rectangular structure. The round house (below, left) is located in Hot Springs, Arkansas.
- **Geodesic dome** homes and buildings were enthusiastically promoted by American architect Buckminster (Bucky) Fuller, as to why the design was efficient and made for easy construction. Dome homes have not caught on, although they can be seen in most parts of the United States. They are a headache for appraisers due to the difficulty in finding comparable sales.

Figure 10.17: Left, Round House, courtesy of Kim DeFilippis; right, Geodesic Dome Home, courtesy of Melanie J. McLane

Log Homes

A style of home that seems to fall into a love/hate category--buyers either love them or hate them—is the log home. Log homes are often a preferred design for second homes, but many elaborate log homes are year-round residences. This photo is of a second home in the mountains.

Figure 10.18: Log Home, Photo courtesy of Melanie J. McLane

Manufactured and Modular Houses

The descendants of the pre-cut houses are today's manufactured and modular houses. There is often confusion between modular and manufactured housing.

MODULAR V. MANUFACTURED HOUSING		
Component	**Modular**	**Manufactured**
Foundation	Designed for crawl space or full basement	Designed for piers, slab
Undercarriage	Wooden with "marriage wall"	Metal, with axles, wheels
Roof pitch	5:12 or greater	3:12
Meter base	On the house	May be on a pole
Framing	2 x 6	2 x 4 (older ones were 1 x 2)
Interior finish	Drywall	Paneling
Windows	Double hung, thermal	Single hung, usually thermal
Doors	Wooden frame and jamb; all doors open to inside	Metal frame and jamb; back door opens out
Cabinets	Wood	Composite materials
Attic	Scuttle	None
Heating system	Designed to be placed in basement or crawl space	Place in a small, specific space
Placement	Placed permanently	Can be moved again

Trailers, or mobile homes, were originally designed to be moved around the countryside as a 'house on wheels.'

- During WWII, these became emergency homes for military people on bases.
- By the 1950s, mobile home parks had arrived, and people were setting up mobile homes to use as permanent houses. Often, they added onto them, making them difficult to move.

Mobile homes became designated as **manufactured housing** on June 15, 1976. The home has to meet these requirements:

- Manufactured after June 15, 1976. Fannie Mae, HUD, and VA will not make loans on manufactured housing constructed *before* this date.
- Installed on a permanent foundation
- Axle and wheels removed
- Appraiser must locate the HUD data plate and HUD Certification plates

In 2015, Fannie Mae made more changes to their requirements for financing a manufactured home:

- Fannie Mae will no longer make loans on manufactured homes that have been moved.
- A move from the dealer's site to the site where it will be financed is acceptable; but should a buyer purchase a manufactured home and put it in a park, and then buy a lot to move it onto, Fannie Mae will not finance the transaction.

The manufactured housing industry keeps adding 'bells and whistles' to their products, blurring the lines between modular and manufactured. For example, manufactured homes used to have only paneling inside and single hung windows. Now, many are being constructed with 2 x 6 walls, drywall interiors, and double hung windows. The major thing to look for is the metal undercarriage, as well as the HUD data plate and the HUD Certification Plates. If the property is a manufactured home, even if it is now on a permanent foundation, with the wheels and axles removed, the appraiser must treat it as manufactured housing, and use a special form for Fannie Mae.

Interior Design Considerations

The basics of design say that a home should be comfortable, and in the words of Fannie Mae, HUD, and VA, "offer spaces for sleeping, living, preparation of meals, and an adequate facility for bathing and disposing of waste." Good design usually involves separating private and public areas of the house. The enduring popularity of the two-story house is credited by some to the floor plan of bedrooms and full baths upstairs, where only the family goes, and living space, kitchen, and at least a half bath downstairs where company can visit and use those rooms.

Layout

Rooms should be laid out so that:

- Doors do not open into each other.
- Access to a bedroom does not go through another bedroom or a bathroom.
- Privacy is not inhibited; for example, half baths opening into a kitchen, dining room, or living room.
- Flow is good from one area to another, especially for entertaining.

Today's buyers like the 'great room' concept of one large room open to the kitchen, as opposed to the formal living rooms and dining rooms of the past.

Storage

Homes should have adequate storage and closet space. However, as costs go up, storage is often one of the first things cut. Compare these two ranch houses:

House #1: Built circa 1961, contains 6 rooms and 11 closets all on the main level. Lower level has a rec room and more storage.

House #2: Built circa 2015, the main level contains a family room, kitchen, master bedroom and bath, and one closet. The lower level has another bedroom, bath, and one more closet. Although both closets are large, they simply do not provide enough storage.

Kitchens

Older kitchens had limited cupboard and counter space, and one sink. Today's upscale kitchens often have more than one sink, islands or other methods of providing generous counter space, and plenty of cupboard space.

Bathrooms

Remember that 40% of American homes did *not* have inside plumbing at the time of World War II. Today, a contractor would never consider building a two bedroom condo without *at least* two baths.

Put another way, buyer expectations have changed--they now expect large bathrooms with vanities, oversized shower stalls, soaker tubs, and in some cases, a bidet. Upscale house plans today usually provide for "en suite" bathrooms for all the bedrooms. But, sometimes, even newer builders do not get it right.

> *For Example*
> A four-bedroom home had a master bedroom with an en suite bath; two other bedrooms with a shared bath between them (sometimes called a "Jack and Jill" bathroom), and on the same floor, a "guest" bedroom. However, due to a poor layout, the guest would have had to go through at least one family member's bedroom to get to a bathroom. Although there was another full bath on the first floor, functionally, buyers want bathrooms on the same level as the bedrooms.

Appraisal Principles and Houses

Some of the considerations appraisers and agents use when pricing houses include highest and best use, functional depreciation or obsolescence, physical depreciation, and economic depreciation or obsolescence. A brief recap of these principles is in order.

Highest and Best Use

Every property has a highest and best use of the site, as if vacant and unimproved. This is based on **PLEM**:

- **Physically** possible,
- **Legally** permissible,
- **Economically** feasible, and
- **Maximally** productive.

In many instances, analysis of highest and best use is fairly simple.

<u>For Example</u>

If a structure is a single-family home, in a neighborhood of other single-family homes, and is zoned single-family residential, *the current use is the highest and best use*. However, that does not mean that the existing structure should remain. In many pricey communities, single-family homes that are solid structures are purchased, torn down, and new, more elaborate houses are built. However, if the zoning is not single family and if the structure appears to lend itself to another use, an analysis of highest and best use is required.

Functional Depreciation

When evaluating homes for sellers or buyers, appraisers need to look at design, layout, storage, and overall functionality of the house. **Functional depreciation or obsolescence** refers to *items that are no longer considered to be adequate by today's standards*. Examples include:

- Bedrooms on levels without bathrooms
- Insufficient bathrooms
- Outdated kitchens and baths
- Poor layout and design
- Inadequate storage

Appraisers will make adjustments for a lack of functionality, or for functional obsolescence.

In appraising, functional obsolescence, or depreciation, is considered either:

- **Curable**
- **Incurable**

The test is how much it would cost to fix the functional problems, and whether that cost would be reflected in additional value. If the "cost to cure" is too great, the value may be land value less demolition costs, meaning the improvement should be torn down and the land redeveloped to its current highest and best use.

Physical Depreciation

Physical Depreciation refers to the wearing out of the structure, or parts of it. The same test applies as is used for functional depreciation: Does the cost to cure equate to an increase in value equal to the cost?

Physical depreciation can be noted in a variety of ways; for example:

- Roofs that are worn out
- Windows that need to be replaced
- Wiring that is worn (which can be both functional and physical)
- HVAC systems that are worn
- Worn floor coverings

Economic Depreciation or External Obsolescence

Economic depreciation or external obsolescence is *always* incurable, because it is based on the location of the house. A house next to a six lane highway, or a sewage treatment plant, is going to suffer a decrease in value because of its location; you cannot cure location.

How to adjust for these differences is a topic for another course. However, very basically, both agents and appraisers look at the market to see how the market treats the differences. This involves research into closed sales to isolate differences between houses.

The REALTORS® Property Resource (RPR ®) is a great tool, because you can 'plug in' differences and the algorithms will supply an answer. RPR® is an automated valuation model, but because it is designed by REALTORS®, for use by REALTORS®, it varies from other AVMs in significant ways: The data is better, because it comes from agents, and the agent has complete control over which comparables to use.

Chapter Summary

1. The 'design' of a house is how it looks and functions (e.g., one-story, two-story, ranch).

2. The 'style' of a house refers to a distinctive appearance (e.g., Cape Cod, Colonial, Victorian, Tudor). Many houses have a mix of architectural styles.

3. One-story houses include ranches, bungalows, and cottages.

4. One-and-a-half story houses have a half story above the first floor. Bungalows and Cape Cod/Cape Ann styles are in this category.

5. Two-story houses span a variety of designs, with older houses having common areas on the main level and private rooms upstairs. In newer homes, master suites are commonly placed on the main floor.

6. Two-and-a-half story houses include Victorian, townhouses, and old row house styles; these houses have a finished upper level.

7. Split-level, bi-level, and raised ranches all have more than one level. Split-level typically has four levels, bi-level has two, and raised ranches have two.

8. Two-family houses are called duplexes, doubles, or twins, depending on the part of the country they're located in.

9. House styles vary widely. Common styles include Federal Period, farm houses, stone houses, Colonial, Colonial half house, Cape Cod, Victorian, Tudor, French Normandy or Provincial, Craftsman, four square, modern, pre-cut, round, octagonal, log, manufactured, and modular.

10. Rooms should be laid out so that doors do not open into each other; access to a bedroom does not go through another bedroom or a bathroom; rooms allow privacy for the inhabitants and avoid things like half baths opening into a kitchen, dining room, or living room; and should allow good flow from one area to another, especially for entertaining.

11. Amenities in houses have changed over the years. Today's kitchens often have more than one sink, islands or other methods of providing generous counter space, and plenty of cupboard space; bedrooms have en suite bathrooms.

12. Every property has a highest and best use of the site, as if vacant and unimproved. This is based on PLEM: Physically possible, legally permissible, economically feasible, and maximally productive.

13. Functional depreciation includes bedrooms on levels without bathrooms, insufficient bathrooms, outdated kitchens and baths, poor layout and design, or inadequate storage. Functional obsolescence, or depreciation, is considered either curable or incurable.

14. Physical depreciation refers to the wearing out of the structure, or parts of it.

15. Economic depreciation or obsolescence is always incurable because it is based on the location of the house.

Chapter Quiz

1. *Which kind of siding has alternating wide boards and narrow strips?*

   a. board and batten

   b. clapboard

   c. cresting

   d. log

2. *Fenestration refers to the*

   a. arrangement of doors and windows in the façade of the house.

   b. corner block or brickwork on a house, which is different than the other materials on the house.

   c. number of trees on the property.

   d. number of windows in the façade of the house.

3. *Which style of home would typically have the most ornamentation?*

   a. Craftsman

   b. Federal Period

   c. Modern

   d. Victorian

4. *Of these styles of houses, which has one-and-a-half stories?*

   a. Cape Ann

   b. Colonial Half

   c. Federal Period

   d. Tudor

5. *Row houses and townhouses*

   a. are often called duplexes.

   b. are strictly found in urban areas.

   c. have only one story.

   d. share common walls between the houses.

6. *Fannie Mae will*

   a. finance manufactured houses that are moved to another location.

   b. make loans on any manufactured house constructed after June 15, 1976.

   c. not accept loans on any manufactured house.

   d. not make loans on manufactured houses constructed before June 15, 1976.

7. *Which is an example of functional obsolescence?*

   a. broken furnace

   b. house next to a power plant

   c. outdated kitchen

   d. worn out carpeting

8. *An example of external obsolescence is a house with*

   a. an airport nearby.

   b. insufficient closet space.

   c. no garage.

   d. a worn out roof.

9. *Which is an example of physical depreciation in a house?*

   a. insufficient closet space

   b. located by a six lane highway

   c. outdated bathroom

   d. windows need replaced

10. *A construction method in which the external walls have exposed wood framing with plaster or brick filling in the space between the framing is called*

    a. board and batten.

    b. cresting.

    c. fenestration.

    d. half timbering.

11. *Which statement about the design and style of houses is TRUE?*

    a. Design refers to a distinctive appearance, whereas style is how a house looks.

    b. A house can have more than one design but only one style.

    c. Style refers to a distinctive appearance, whereas design is how a house looks.

    d. The terms 'design' and 'style' can be used interchangeably.

Glossary

ABS (Acrylonitrile Butadiene Styrene) A type of plastic pipe and fittings used in plumbing; more rigid than PVC, but will deform if exposed to sunlight.

Adobe Among the earliest of building materials where soil, dung or straw, and water are made into bricks.

Alternating Current (AC) An electric current that reverses direction at regular intervals.

Aluminum In construction, a siding material made from aluminum that has a baked-on enamel finish.

Ampere (Amp) The basic unit of electrical current.

Asbestos A fibrous material derived from a naturally occurring group of minerals; used in building materials for both its natural insulating properties and fire resistance.

Attic Baffles A building product made of strips of a foam product that is installed on the inside of the attic roof, which allows air to circulate from the soffit through the attic. This prevents the insulation from making the house too air tight, causing indoor air pollution and moisture problems. Also called **Rafter Vents**, **Channel Vents**, **Vent Chutes**, and other names.

Awning Window A window hinged at the top that opens out from the building, commonly found in basements.

Backflow Preventer A check valve installed on the public water supply to prevent any contaminated water from a house from entering the public water main.

Balloon Framing A technique of framing where the long vertical pieces (studs) are installed in a continuous piece from foundation to roof line.

Balusters Small posts or pillars, often decorative, in a series that support an upper rail. Also called **Spindles**.

Balustrade A rail and the row of balusters that support it. Seen on porches and staircases and found in a variety of architectural styles.

Baseboard Heat A heating system covered with a panel that is affixed horizontally along the baseboard of a wall. Can be a hot water or electric system.

Beam A long piece of timber (or metal) that spans an opening or part of a building, and provides support to a roof or floor above it. Beams are installed horizontally.

Blackwater Wastewater from toilets.

Bleeding A method to remove excess trapped air in a hot water heating system.

Blueboard A type of drywall with a distinctive blue paper covering on which specially formulated plaster is applied.

Board and Batten Siding A type of siding that has alternating wide boards and narrow wooden strips called battens.

Boiler An enclosed vessel in which water is heated and circulated, either as hot water or as steam, for heating or power.

Brass A yellow metal made by combining copper and zinc; used for water supply lines and fittings.

Brick A building material used either as a veneer, or in double or triple brick construction.

Building Envelope The entire building from footer to roof. It encloses the living area and should provide protection from the elements.

Carbon Monoxide A natural byproduct of fuel combustion; a colorless, odorless gas released as fuel sources break down to produce heat.

Casement Window A window hinged, usually on the side, that can open outward or inward.

Cast Iron A hard metal made from alloy, carbon, and silicon that is cast into shape; widely used in plumbing supply lines and waste lines.

Ceiling Tiles Tiles that are hung from a metal grid or installed directly onto a ceiling. Ceiling tiles are made of a variety of materials; some may contain asbestos.

Cesspool An underground container for storage of household wastewater; in the form of a concrete or metal tank, or a tank lined with logs, railroad ties, or concrete blocks.

Circuit Breaker An automatically operated electrical switch designed to protect an electrical circuit from damage caused by overcurrent/overload or short circuit. Its basic function is to interrupt current flow after protective relays detect a fault.

Circuit Panel A component of an electricity supply system that divides an electrical power feed into subsidiary circuits, while providing a protective fuse or circuit breaker for each circuit, in a common enclosure. Also called a **Breaker Panel or Box**.

Circulating Motor A motor used to circulate hot water or steam through the system of a house; it can also allow for different heating zones.

Clay Tile A roofing tile of fired earthenware clay.

Clerestory Window A window located high on a high wall, above eye level.

Column A vertical post supporting a roof or other portions of a house. Columns are categorized by design: Doric, Ionic, Corinthian, Tuscan, and Composite. They are often associated with Greek Revival architecture.

Composition Asphalt A siding material made of colored granules glued to asphalt; this material was widely used from the 1930s through the 1950s.

Concrete or Cement Siding A durable siding material made of concrete fibers and other materials.

Conduction The transfer of heat from one area to another by the use of solids.

Convection The transfer of heat from one area to another by the use of liquids.

Copper A reddish-brown colored metal; used in electrical wiring and plumbing pipes.

Cornice The overhanging section just below the roof, and in Victorian and other architecture, an ornamental piece. The function of the cornice overhang is to protect the structure's walls. The cornice is traditionally by definition decorative.

CPVC (Chlorinated Polyvinyl Chloride) A type of pipe used in plumbing for cold and hot water; can withstand high temperatures making it suitable for hot water lines.

Creosote The by-product of burning wood, which includes smoke, water vapor, gases, unburned wood particles, hydrocarbon, tar fog, and assorted minerals. As these substances move up the chimney flue, which is colder than the stove, condensation occurs and produces a residue of these items.

Cresting A decorative feature at the roof line or roof ridge, often found on Victorian homes. It can be wrought iron or a balustrade.

Direct Current (DC) An electric current flowing in only one direction. Direct current can be produced by a power source, batteries, solar cells, or dynamos.

Double Hung Window A window where both the lower sash goes up and the upper sash goes down.

Drain-Waste-Vent (DWV) System A system that removes greywater and blackwater from a building and vents air from the wastewater pipes out of the house.

Drywall A building material made by putting a sheet of gypsum board between two sheets of heavy paper. Also called **Plasterboard**, **Wallboard**, or **Gypsum Board**.

Duct Tubes, canals, pipes, and vents used in a heating system to carry warm air to the house, and cold air back to the furnace.

Encapsulation The process of applying a sealant to asbestos-containing material, which penetrates the material's surface, preventing the release of the dangerous fibers.

Energy Efficient Mortgage (EEM) A mortgage that credits a home's energy efficiency in the mortgage itself. EEMs give borrowers the opportunity to finance cost-effective, energy-saving measures as part of a single mortgage and stretch debt-to-income qualifying ratios on loans, thereby allowing borrowers to qualify for a larger loan amount and a better and more energy-efficient home.

Energy Guide Labels The yellow stickers affixed to products to advise the consumer of both the projected energy consumption of that particular product, and the average energy consumption for other products like it.

ENERGY STAR One of the rating systems available to evaluate homes for energy efficiency. ENERGY STAR raters are RESNET approved.

Expansion Tank A small tank used to protect hot water heating systems from excessive pressure. The tank allows steam or hot water to expand and prevents rupturing of the pipes and fittings.

Fenestration The arrangement of doors and windows in the facade of a building.

Fiberglass Shingles A roofing product made the same way as asphalt shingles, except that the base is made of fiberglass.

Fixed Window A window that does not move at all; often found as picture windows.

Flat Roof A roof with a minimal pitch that allows water to drain off.

Flue A duct, pipe, or opening in a chimney that allows the smoke and waste gases to escape.

Footer The support for the foundation of a building. Footers are installed below the frost line, and are wider than the foundations that they support.

Foundation The support for a building. It can be constructed of stone, poured concrete, pre-engineered concrete walls, concrete block, or even wood.

Friable When asbestos, or the material containing asbestos, crumbles, pulverizes, or reduces to powder by moderate pressure.

Fuse A device containing a conductor that melts when excess current runs through an electric circuit, opening and thereby protecting the circuit.

Gabel A roof having a single slope on each side of a central ridge and a gable at one or both ends; most common style of roof.

Galvanized Steel A metal used for both supply and waste lines.

Gambrel Roof A roof that has two pitches on each side (change in slope partway up the roof); often seen on barns.

Gargoyle A carved or formed grotesque animal, serpent, or human usually made of stone or concrete and placed near the roof; often formed with a spout and used to divert water from buildings; can be found on churches or elaborate residential properties.

Green 1) A word widely and loosely used to describe the use, in construction, of renewable materials; 2) non-toxic materials, and sometimes locally produced materials, usually with an energy efficient component.

Greenwashing The practice of touting a product or program as environmentally friendly, when in fact, it is not.

Greywater Household water that comes from sinks, bathtubs, dishwashers, and washing machines; it does not contain human waste.

Griffin A mythical animal that is half eagle and half lion; sometimes found on ornate residential structures.

Ground Fault Circuit Interrupter (GFCI) A device installed in an electrical outlet that shuts off an electric power circuit when it detects that current is flowing along an unintended path. GFCIs are required by code to be in kitchens, baths, and other areas of the house.

Grounding A safety measure to help prevent electrical shock by use of 'grounding rods' to direct electric current into the ground in the event of a lighting strike, or other mishap.

Gypsum A soft sulfate mineral, used in blackboard chalk and in plaster and drywall.

Half Timber (Half Timbering) A construction method in which the external walls have exposed wood framing constructed of timber frames, with other materials such as plaster or brick filling the space between them.

HERS (Home Energy Rating Systems) The index used by Certified HERS Raters. In the HERS rating system, the higher the score, the less efficient the home is. For example, a 0 = a zero net energy home produces all of the energy it consumes.

Hip Roof A roof that has four slopes, with two that are shorter and triangular.

Hollow-core Door A door (usually interior) where sandwiched between a thin press-board or wood veneer exterior is a cardboard honeycomb. Hollow core doors can be flush or have raised panels.

Hopper Window A window similar to an awning window, except it is often hinged at the bottom and opens into the building; commonly found in basements.

ICC (International Code Council) A member-focused association dedicated to helping the building safety community and construction industry provide safe, sustainable, and affordable construction through the development of codes and standards used in the design, build, and compliance process. Most U.S. communities and many global markets choose the International Codes.

Infestation Usually from insects, one of the many things that can compromise the building envelope.

Inglenook A space with a seat on either side of a large fireplace.

Insulating Concrete Forms (ICFs) A construction system made with lightweight foam forms (blocks, panels, and planks) that are stacked together and filled with concrete. The forms remain permanently in place and provide insulation to the structure.

Jalousie Window A window of slats of glass, moved with a crank; often seen on older storm doors, porch doors, and windows.

Joists Long beams of wood or steel that span the piers of a foundation or the load bearing walls of a roof.

Junction Box A plastic or metal container for electrical connections, usually intended to conceal them from sight and deter tampering.

Lally Column A post, made of metal, with a screw type device at the top, designed to be placed in a basement to provide additional support for the house.

Lath Thin, flat strips of wood used to hold plaster to walls or ceilings.

Lead A mineral used in pipes and paint, as well as other products, including glazes on ceramic tiles. In sufficient quantities, lead is carcinogenic.

LEED (Leadership in Energy Efficiency and Design) A third party rating system for energy efficiency. The USGBC (United States Green Building Council) confers LEED designations.

Luan (or Lauan) Wood from a number of tropical southeast Asian trees, which varies in color from light yellow to reddish-brown or brown. Luan is used as an underlayment under carpeting and in the construction of hollow core doors. Also called **Philippine Mahogany**.

Mansard Roof A roof that has two distinct slopes with the lower one steeper than the upper one, often with a flat roof on top.

Masonite® A brand name for hardboard siding made by mixing wood chips with glue.

Masonry A general term referring to concrete, concrete block, brick, and stucco construction.

Mast A rigid, hollow pole with a service cap on top of it, typically installed on the roof or the upper side of an outside wall.

Metal Roof A roofing system made from metal panels or pieces.

Muntins and Mullions The strips of wood (or other materials) separating panes of glass in a window. The muntins are vertical and the mullions are horizontal.

NAHB (National Association of Home Builders) A large trade group made up of home builders; they also have a research center that helped the ICC develop standards for Green Building.

New Deal A series of domestic programs enacted by the U.S. between 1933 and 1938. The programs were in response to the Great Depression and focused on relief, recovery, and return.

Nob-and-Tube Wiring A type of wiring commonly used decades ago where open electric wires are supported on knobs and encased in tubes in areas where they pass through beams or partitions.

Orangeburg® A waste pipe material made of lightweight wood fibers, adhesive, and coal tar, which were bound together; commonly used during the 1950s and 1960s. Also called **Fiber Conduit**.

Oriented Strand Board (OSB) An engineered wood particle board that is glued and compressed.

Paneling A building material that comes in panels in a variety of materials—from solid wood paneling to fiberboard paneling, and some laminated paneling that resembles wallpaper. The thickness, durability, and cost all vary.

PB (Polybutylene) A type of plastic piping used in plumbing from the 1970s through 1990; due to defective issues, it is no longer sold.

PEX Crosslinked polyethylene tubing, usually seen in blue (cold water) and red (hot water) as supply lines. Also used as tubing for radiant floor heating.

Plaster A soft, thick mixture of lime or gypsum, sand, water, and sometimes hair or other fiber, applied when wet and dries in place. Also called **Horsehair Plaster**.

Platform Framing A technique of framing where a platform is built over the basement or crawl space, and then studs are extended up to the next level, where another platform is built; finally studs are extended to the roof line.

Post A long piece of timber or metal is installed vertically that supplies support for horizontal pieces, such as beams.

Potable Suitable for drinking.

Pressure Relief Valve A valve found on hot water and steam systems, as well as on water heaters, which releases steam and pressure should the temperature inside the furnace, boiler, or hot water heater get too hot.

PVC Polyvinyl chloride, used for drain lines and some supply lines.

Quoin A block or brickwork on the corner of a building that is used for reinforcement or decorative use; usually constructed of different materials from the walls.

R-Value A measure of thermal resistance used in the building and construction industry. 'R' stands for resistance. The higher the R-value, the greater the insulating capability.

Radiant Heat Heat energy that is transmitted by electromagnetic waves; not transmitted by conduction or convection.

Radiator A heating device consisting of a series of connected pipes, typically inside an upright metal structure, through which steam or hot water is circulated, and radiates heat into the surrounding space.

Radon A naturally occurring radioactive gas that emanates from rocks, soil, and water due to the decay of uranium.

Rafters Sloped support beams that follow the pitch of the roof and serve to hold the outer roof covering.

RESNET (Residential Energy Specialists Network) A group that performs energy efficiency ratings on homes, and trains individuals to be RESNET raters.

Ridge Beam A structural member at the top of the roof used to support the ends of the rafters at the ridge.

Ridge Vent A vent running horizontally along the ridge, at the highest point of the roof where two or more planes come together.

Rise The distance from the attic floor to the peak of the roof.

Roof Pitch A numerical measure of the steepness of a roof. The roof's vertical rise is divided by the horizontal span (or run), expressed as a ratio of the number of inches of incline per each 12 inches, with the rise followed by the run (e.g., 3:12).

Roof Trusses A framework of rafters, posts, and beams that forms the support for a roof.

Run The distance from the center to the edge of the roof. The runs added together equal the span.

Saltbox Roof A roof that is shorter in the front and slopes down in the back; the front is two stories and the back is one story.

Septic System A system for disposing of sewage where there is not access to public sewer. Septic systems vary from cesspools by having drain fields.

Service Entrance The point where electricity enters a house from the power supplied and goes into the meter.

Sheathing A layer of boards or other wood or fiber materials applied to the outer studs, joists, and rafters to strengthen the structure and serve as a base for exterior weatherproof covering.

Shed Roof A flat roof that slopes in one direction; often used on porch roofs, or additions to houses.

Single Hung Window A window where only the bottom part moves up and down and the upper part is fixed.

Slate Roof A roof made of slate layers, tiles, or plates.

Sliding Window A window that slides from one side to the other to allow fresh air.

Soffit The finished underside of the overhanging edge of a roof.

Soil Types A reference to the types of soil houses are built on; homes must be properly engineered for the soil type.

Span The entire length from one side of a building to the other.

Spire A tapering roof, or an ornamental metal piece on top of a tower or turret.

Stone A building material used for walls and foundations in old houses; imitation or engineered stone siding is available today.

Storm Window A window installed to offer weather protection and more insulation.

Straw Bale In construction, a building method using bales of straw. Walls constructed of straw bales have a stucco-like finish installed over them as an exterior finish.

Stucco A building material made of aggregates, a binder, and water, which is applied over mesh, usually on top of masonry or wood.

Supply Lines The lines that supply water to the fixtures. Sinks, washing machines, bathtubs, and showers all have both hot and cold supply lines; toilets typically have only cold supply lines.

Swamp Cooler A type of air conditioning system that runs air over saturated pads.

Thermal Window A window that has two or more layers of glass, with an inert gas between the panes. The most commonly used gas is argon; more expensive windows use krypton gas.

Thermostat A device used to regulate the heat or air conditioning coming from the system.

Trap A part of plumbing fixtures designed to hold water and keep sewer gas from coming up into the house. Also called "U," "S," or "J" traps.

Triple Track Storm and Screen Combination A window that contains two panes of glass (upper and lower), as well as a screen. During warm weather, the extra panes of glass can be slid up and the screen slid down, allowing fresh air to get into the house.

Turret A small tower on a building.

U-Value A measure of the heat transmission through a window or door. 'U' stands for unit. The lower the U-value, the greater the insulating capability.

Urea-formaldehyde A thermosetting synthetic resin made from urea and formaldehyde; used in the manufacturing of building materials, and home products such as particleboard, plywood paneling, carpeting, and ceiling tiles.

VCP (Vitrified Clay Pipe) A pipe made from a mixture of clay that has been subjected to very high temperatures, thus "vitrifying" the pipe, which makes it a hard, inert ceramic; used in sewer pipes. The manufacturing process has been fine-tuned for centuries and was designed to be fiscally responsible, which had the added benefit of being environmentally responsible. But the primary benefit of using VCP in sanitary sewers is its long service life.

Vent Pipe A pipe (often plastic) that regulates air pressure in plumbing and keeps sewer gas from building up inside the system. Vent pipes are often stacked.

Vinyl A durable siding material that comes in many colors, and is relatively inexpensive. Continues to be popular in home construction today.

Volatile Organic Compounds (VOCs) Gases emitted from certain solids or liquids; organic chemicals found in many household products.

Volts A measure of electric potential. This is the energy that could be released if the electric current is allowed to flow.

Waste Lines The lines that carry used water from the drains into the sewer or septic system.

Weep Holes Holes deliberately made in brick veneer applications to carry moisture away from the building and to equalize air pressure.

Zoning The distribution of heat in a house to control temperature levels in various rooms. In hot water systems, zone valves control the distribution of the hot water and the output of heat.